It's another Quality Book from CGP

This book is for anyone getting ready for the KS3 English SATs.

It contains lots of tricky questions designed
to make you sweat — because that's the only
way you'll get any better.

It's also got some daft bits in to try and make
the whole experience at least vaguely
entertaining for you.

What CGP is all about

Our sole aim here at CGP is to produce the highest quality
books — carefully written, immaculately presented and
dangerously close to being funny.

Then we work our socks off to get them out to you
— at the cheapest possible prices.

Contents

THE SHAKESPEARE TEST

ANSWERS

Published by Coordination Group Publications, Ltd.

Contributors:

Taissa Csáky   Chris Dennett   Tim Major   Katherine Reed   Ed Robinson

ISBN: 978 1 84146 290 5
Groovy website: www.cgpbooks.co.uk
Jolly bits of clipart from CorelDRAW®
Printed by Elanders Hindson Ltd, Newcastle upon Tyne
With thanks to Paula Barnett, Ed Robinson, Glenn Rogers, Rachel Selway and Dan Owen for the proofreading.
Design, layout, original illustrations and original text © Coordination Group Publications Ltd. 2003

Reading — The Basics

Finding Facts

There's always a tasty bunch of fact-finding questions in the SATs. You just have to find the right bit in the text and write down the info — you couldn't ask for a nicer start to the SATs really.

An extract from a magazine article about the HB Animation Studio

The HB Animation Studio was founded in 1998 by Managing Director Harold Black, and since then it has become a hugely successful business. In the beginning, it was just Harold working alone in his attic room, but now the company employs 230 people in jobs ranging from scriptwriters to cooks!

The secret of HB's success has always been the quality of its 3-D animation. Characters are carefully shaped from ordinary modelling clay, and are usually no more than 20 centimetres tall. More complex characters have wire frames (or rod-and-joint structures called armatures) inside the clay. These allow the model to be adjusted very accurately.

The really time-consuming part of the job is actually filming — in order for the characters' movements to appear realistic, 24 pictures (or 'frames') need to be taken to put together 1 second of finished film!

Q1 Copy and complete the table using information from the magazine article above.

Description	Fact
Year HB Animation Studio was created	
Founded by...	
Harold Black's current position	
Total number of employees today	

Q2 What is the normal maximum height of HB's characters?

Q3 What must be included in models that need very accurate adjustment?

Q4 What are 'armatures'?

Q5 How many frames per second need to be filmed? Choose from options i)-iv).

　　i) 20　　　ii) 230　　　iii) 24　　　iv) 25

Q6 Why is this number of frames per second needed?

You don't need to write loads — just write out the bit of the text that answers the question.

Q7 According to the writer, what is the secret of HB's success?

Finding the Important Bits

The first thing to do with any reading question is to dig out the bit of the text that tells you the answer to the question. Then lick it clean and give it a good chew. Or just write it down.

> An extract from the story *Carrie's Life of Piracy*
>
> Carrie darted round the corner into a dingy side street full of discarded wooden crates. She was closely followed by Ben, who stopped and bent over, panting. He felt like he'd been out of breath ever since they'd left the Pirate Academy.
>
> "Come on, Ben! We have to keep moving — otherwise they'll send us back, and you know what that means..."
>
> Suddenly they were aware of a shadow looming over them. Carrie gasped and looked up towards the leering, cruel face of Captain Hack.
>
> "Aaah, my dear pupils," said Hack, relishing each word, "I'm only performing my duty as your tutor. You know that any student failing to hand in homework must walk the plank."
>
> Carrie and Ben exchanged a glance. Ben dashed forward with a yell, and managed to slip between Captain Hack's legs. Before Hack could react, Ben ripped a thin plank of wood from a nearby crate.
>
> "Carrie! Catch!" he shouted, and tossed the plank over Hack's head, to be caught by Carrie.
>
> For a moment Carrie looked at the plank, bemused. Then she remembered her sword-fighting lessons, and crouched with the plank in her hand, ready to defend herself against her pirate tutor.

Q1   Write out the part of the text where you are told about the following things.

a)   Where Carrie and Ben arrive at the start of the extract.

b)   How Ben feels at the beginning of the extract.

c)   Where Carrie and Ben have come from.

d)   What Captain Hack looks like.

e)   How Captain Hack wants to punish Carrie and Ben.

f)   What Carrie and Ben did that needs to be punished.

g)   How Ben escapes from Captain Hack.

h)   Where Ben got the thin plank of wood from.

Umm... I'd better head back. Reports to write, homework to mark...

Q2   How do Carrie and Ben know that Captain Hack has arrived? Write out the part of the text that tells you.

Q3   What is Carrie about to do with the thin plank of wood? Write out the part of the text that tells you.

Trapped in a snow poem — it was phrasing...

If you can pick out useful phrases from texts really quickly, then you'll have bags of time left for important things like looking out of the window and picking your nose. And answering questions.

Artists against rabbits

Backing Up Points

You have to back up your answers, otherwise you haven't proved they're right.
The trick is to always make a **COMMENT**, give **EVIDENCE** from the text, then **EXPLAIN** what it means.

Questions 1-3 are about the following short extract.

> "I think we should get rid of the whole stinking lot," said Hanif, pointing at the rabbits.

Q1   Write a sentence commenting on how Hanif feels about the rabbits.

Q2   Which of the following sentences uses evidence from
the extract to show how Hanif feels about the rabbits?

i)   Hanif wants to get rid of the rabbits.

ii)   Hanif wants to get rid of the rabbits. He shouts, which shows he doesn't like them.

iii) Hanif wants to get rid of the rabbits. He calls them "stinking", which shows that he
doesn't like them.

Q3   What does this tell the reader about Hanif? Copy out the correct answer.

i)   Hanif has a strong opinion about the rabbits.

ii)   Hanif is depressed and hates everything in the world.

iii) Hanif is a bully who goes around annoying other people.

Make Tea
Not Rabbits

Get lost rabbits

Questions 4-6 are about the extract below.

> Milla glanced around the street nervously before she dumped the envelope into the bin.

Q4   What is Milla's mood in this extract?

Q5   Write out the part of the text that backs up your answer to Q4.

Q6   What does this tell the reader about Milla? Copy out the correct answer.

i)   Milla doesn't like using bins in the street.

ii)   Milla seems to be worried that someone will see her dumping the envelope into the bin.

iii) Milla doesn't care what anyone thinks about her dumping the envelope into the bin.

Question 7 is about the extract below.

> "I'll be fine — don't worry about me," said Miles, with the hint of a tear in his eye.

Q7   How is Miles feeling in this extract? Write about Miles' character in your answer.
Give evidence from the text in your answer and explain how it proves your point.

Summarising

If you're asked to summarise the points made in a text, it means that you need to write the important bits out <u>in your own words</u>. And don't waffle — summarising means using less words.

An extract from the story *Felix and the Dragon's Revenge*

The elderly King looked down his nose at the men assembled before him.

"Do you mean to tell me that they *all* went free?" he thundered.

Felix remained on his knees and let out a gentle sob. The King, becoming somewhat reflective, turned and gazed vacantly out of the tall window.

"It wasn't always like this," he muttered. "During the reign of my father, captured knights had some respect and *stayed* captured. Aaah, my father. What it was to be a child. I used to play in that very garden. Haha! The fun I had with my wooden horse... Ahem. Anyway, it just won't do, there have been too many daring escapes recently."

Felix was about to interrupt, but the King's courtier placed a hand on his shoulder to stop him.

"And you," began the King, his voiced raised and turning to face Felix, "You have done nothing to stop these knights!" He gestured to Prime Minister Katan. "Tie Felix up, take him to Vertis Ledge, and let the dragons do as they wish."

As Felix was being dragged away by two burly attendants, he found the strength to cry out, "You'll see, my lord! One of these days the dragons will come after you!"

Q1   Make a list of all the characters mentioned in the text.   *Hint: some of the characters' names aren't given.*

Q2   Which of the characters actually speak in the text?

Q3   Copy out and correct this summary of the paragraph starting "It wasn't always like this..."

The King remembers when his father was king, and knights were harder to control. He decides that something must be done about the knights. Then he starts to think about his childhood when he played with his toys in the garden.   *Hint: There are two big errors.*

Q4   Copy out the sentence that describes the King's mood in the fourth paragraph.

i)   He seems angry with Felix, and keeps shouting at him.

ii)   He seems angry with Felix, but is easily distracted by memories of his childhood.

iii)   He talks about his childhood and doesn't care about the knights at all.

Q5   Summarise the paragraph starting "And you," in your own words.

Q6   Write a summary of the whole text. Your summary should be no more than five sentences long, and you'll have to decide which of the details on this page need to be included.

In winter I yodel — in summar i sing...

Summarising is dead handy even if a question doesn't ask you to do it specifically. If you're grappling with a nightmare text, try retelling the story to yourself, as simply as you can.

Different Types of Text

As soon as you start reading a text in the SATs you should be thinking about what <u>type</u> of text it is. Then straightaway you'll be thinking about the kind of questions they'll ask.

A Five per cent of the population will suffer from an epileptic seizure at some time in their life, *writes Gareth Johns*. Epilepsy affects 450,000 people in the UK, usually under-20-year-olds and those over 60. Seizures involve loss of consciousness and may affect memory or mood.

B Watching the tutting clock,
Only six more minutes until I can be
    there and not *here*.
Gazing out through dusty panes,
Following the inkblot shadows of
    clouds with my eyes.
Outside, sunlight plays on the ground
    like excitable children,
And a bird shouts with happiness.

C Toby proceeded to mow the lawn like a man resigned to a long stretch in prison.

Being a man of unimaginable dullness, his only reaction when his wife bellowed that she was leaving him was to gently let the engine sputter to a forlorn halt. All that remained was a glacial silence, and a partially cut lawn.

D In order to get the best results from your T-300 kitchen juicer, please note the following points:
1) Always make a clear space around the T-300 in case of juice spray.
2) Avoid juicing soft fruits such as bananas. The residue may be difficult to clear from the workings of the T-300.

Q1   Copy out each title below and write down which of the texts each goes with — A, B, C or D.

   <u>Epilepsy — The Facts</u>   <u>Using your T-300</u>   <u>Waiting</u>   <u>A Man Alone</u>

Q2   Which texts are examples of non-fiction?

Q3   Which texts feature very descriptive language?

Q4   Write out each of the labels below and decide whether they apply to A, B, C or D.

   Poem   Story   Manual   Magazine article

Q5   Match each of the questions below to one of the texts — A, B, C or D.

   a)   Describe the ways that the writer has made his points clear in the text.
   b)   Explain how the writer contrasts indoors and outdoors in the text.
   c)   How does the writer use facts and figures to back up his points?
   d)   How does the writer show that the main character is lonely?

You don't actually have to <u>do</u> the questions.

Reading — The Basics

Working Out What's Going On

The texts in the SATs aren't always that easy — some of them are downright confusing. Examiners often ask you to work out what's happened or what might happen next.

> An extract from the short story *Mrs Hanrahan's Holiday*
>
> Ever since she'd woken to shrill beeps that still echoed around her head, Mrs Hanrahan's day had got worse and worse. She'd had to spend a few hours hunting for the tickets — knowing that without them she *definitely* wouldn't be going on holiday today. She'd finally located the tickets beneath the tottering pile of dirty dishes, but hadn't retrieved them safely before sacrificing two of the dishes to the floor in a flurry of ceramic and congealed Chinese takeaway.
>
> Finally, Mrs Hanrahan was ready.
>
> "Bags packed – check. Tickets – check. House keys – check," she murmured. She placed the front door keys carefully on top of the tickets. With a grimace, Mrs Hanrahan suddenly remembered to put the milk bottles outside. She abandoned her luggage, collected the bottles, wrote a quick note to the milkman and then ventured outside. Just as she placed the bottles by the front doormat, Mrs Hanrahan was aware of the sound of the front door latch clicking behind her...

Q1   Copy and complete this table to show the order of the events in the extract.

Event	Order in extract
Looks for tickets	
Puts milk bottles outside	
Wakes up	1
Has an accident in the kitchen	
Puts front door keys with tickets	

The "Why me?" Coalition Protest Against Tidying

Q2   Write out the part of the text that gives you a clue about what kind of tickets Mrs Hanrahan is searching for.

Q3   Write out the part of the text that tells you about the accident in the first paragraph.

Q4   Copy out the answer that best describes the accident.

i)   Mrs Hanrahan ate some Chinese takeaway, and then dropped a plate.

ii)   Mrs Hanrahan knocked over two dirty dishes, and they smashed on the floor.

iii) Mrs Hanrahan knocked over two dirty dishes, and they landed in the bin.

Q5   What happens as Mrs Hanrahan is putting the milk bottles outside?

Q6   Write a paragraph explaining what you think might happen next in the story.

Working Out What's Going On

Questions that ask you to work out what's happening can also refer to non-fiction texts.
Sometimes you need to work out what technical language means, by looking at the sentences around it.

> An extract from a magazine article about manual photography

Many of us are used to just pointing, pressing, and getting someone else to do the dirty work. However, using manual cameras takes a bit more thought and preparation. Are you up to the challenge?

Firstly, you need to decide what type of film to use. 'Slow' films are suitable for normal lighting, whereas you'll need to use a faster ISO 400 film to take pictures on gloomy days (or as fast as ISO 1000 if it's night-time).

Once you've loaded the film, you've got to think about camera settings before you start snapping. Changing the aperture setting affects the amount of light that comes into the camera — if it's a bright scene then make the aperture narrower, if it's a dark scene then the aperture needs to be larger.

Next comes shutter speed settings (the amount of time the shutter stays open when you press the button). A long shutter speed not only lets in a lot of light, it also means that any moving objects will be blurred — useful for arty action shots but not so good if you want lots of fine detail. If you're not using a camera with automatic focus, you'll need to rotate the focusing ring before you take the picture.

Of course, the next step is getting the pictures developed — you can either send the film away to a laboratory, or you can develop the pictures yourself in a darkroom.

Next week — darkroom secrets

Q1 What does 'pointing, pressing, and getting someone else to do the dirty work' in the introduction to the text mean?

Q2 Which of the things below explains what ISO refers to? Write out the bit of text that tells you.

film size   film speed   lighting conditions   sugary sports drinks

Q3 Which of the film speeds below is a 'slow' film? Explain how you worked it out.

ISO 1000   ISO 400   ISO 100   ISO 1600

Q4 What do you think the line 'Next week — darkroom secrets' refers to?

Q5 David wants to take detailed action pictures of a sports day outside in the sunlight. Copy this table and fill it in to show the settings that David should use.

Camera setting	Set to...	Reason
Film speed		
Aperture setting		
Shutter speed		

Q6 Emily wants to take blurry pictures of a jazz band playing in a dingy bar. Draw a table similar to the one in Q5 and fill it in to show the settings that she should use.

Q7 Why do you think the writer has described using manual cameras as a 'challenge'? Write a paragraph, and refer to the extract to back up your answer.

SAT-STYLE QUESTION

(5 marks)

Working Out How Characters Feel

Examiners also like asking you about how characters <u>feel</u> about what's happening. You need to put yourself in the character's shoes for a bit, and hope that they're not full of toe jam.

> An extract from the story *Sir Lancelot's Quest*
>
> Sir Lancelot sighed deeply and gazed upward at the falcon circling overhead. It was free to soar where it wished, whereas he had to trudge grimly ahead through the forest, towards Camelot and the king he had wished never to see again. All of a sudden, fatigue hit him. The battle with Sir Phelot had been a hard one, and now Sir Lancelot almost wished that he himself had been slain, if only to be finally at peace.
>
> The journey had been long and difficult. Many times Lancelot had been forced to hack his way wearily through dense foliage with his sword, had waded through rivers and then walked for hours in sodden clothes, and had bloodied his hands from battles with countless honourable knights.

Q1   Write out the part of the text that tells you why Lancelot doesn't want to go to Camelot.

Q2   Copy out the answer that best describes why Sir Lancelot is jealous of the falcon.

   i)   Lancelot wishes he was free to go where he wanted and didn't have to walk any more.

   ii) Lancelot wishes he could fly to Camelot instead of walking.

   iii) Lancelot wishes he could get a better view from above the trees.

Hi Arthur, mate, sos about that thing with your wife... No. Sorry Arthur, please believe me... No.

Q3   The extract starts "Sir Lancelot sighed deeply". Write down two other things Lancelot does that show how he is feeling.

Q4   Why does Lancelot almost wish that he had been killed by Sir Phelot?

Q5   Match up the things that happened on the journey, to how they would have made Lancelot feel.

What happened	**How it would have made Lancelot feel**
Had to cut through dense foliage	Sad because he respected them
Waded through rivers and walked in wet clothes	Tired and frustrated
Killed many other knights	Uncomfortable

Q6   Write a paragraph explaining how you think Sir Lancelot would have felt at the end of his journey to Camelot. Use your answers to the other questions to back up your points.

How to get rid of boils — Lancelot...

The questions on the last three pages are all about ways of figuring out what's happening in texts that aren't 100% clear. Questions like these always come up in the SATs, so get practising now.

Descriptions

Exam questions often ask you to write about the way things are described in the text. You've got to be able to work out what information a description gives you, and the effect it has on the reader.

An extract from the novella *The Case of the Missing Relic*

Tonight, the whole city seemed peaceful. Even the birds were asleep, and not a sound disturbed the eerie quiet. The river flowed gently past the houses as if it didn't want to wake up the slumbering inhabitants.

Inspector Graham paced the streets, expecting trouble at any moment. He gazed up at the pale moon which lit the streets below, and held his gas lamp out with a trembling hand. In front of him he could make out the grey archway of a narrow doorway. The night before he had come across a pack of snarling dogs guarding the doorway, but tonight they were absent. The door opened with a low creak at his push, and the lamp cast a flickering glow over the dim inside of the room. The only furniture was a broad farmhouse table, upon which were several items — a cotton glove, a faded yellow sheet of paper, and a small stone carving of a man crouching as if about to pounce at the Inspector.

Q1 Copy and complete the table about the way things are described in the extract above.

Thing being described	How it's described
	Peaceful
	Flickering
The doorway	
The dogs guarding the doorway	
	Faded and yellow
Inspector Graham's hand	
The inside of the room	

Q2 Which of the descriptions from the table in Q1 make the things sound scary?

Q3 Write out the part of the text that describes the stone carving.

Q4 Write out the statement that explains the effect of the description in Q3.

i) The statue is described as if it is alive — this effect is called alliteration.

ii) The statue is described as if it is alive — this effect is called metaphor.

iii) The statue is described as if it is alive — this effect is called personification.

Q5 Write out another part of the text that uses the same effect.

Q6
SAT-STYLE QUESTION
How does the writer of *The Case of the Missing Relic* use descriptions to make the story scary? Use your answers to the questions on this page to help you.

(5 marks)

Descriptions of Characters

Page 11
Take 5

Writers tell you about characters through the way they're described — the things they say and the things they do. I bet you can spot descriptions a mile away, but practise <u>writing</u> about them too.

An extract from the novel *The Movie Murders*

"...and cut!"

David Hodgson had been directing his film *Curl Girl* for almost eight months now, and it was beginning to get the better of him. He wheeled around abruptly on his heel towards his fresh-faced assistant Sarah, who surveyed him with a slightly pitying look.

"Have the extras arrived yet?" asked David in a shaky voice. He grabbed Sarah by the lapels of her smart jacket. Sarah tried to keep smiling, but failed. "And *where* is our leading lady?" demanded David, as he started to pull at the few tufts of greying hair left on his head, his eyes darting from side to side as if following the path of a wasp.

"Your ravishing, immensely talented leading lady has just entered the building," said a silky voice from the darkness. A figure sauntered casually into the light — it was none other than Denise Penrith. She tossed back her mane of honey-coloured hair and fixed David with a commanding gaze. Denise continued in a steady, alluring tone, "and I would like to talk to you about my fees."

Q1   Write out the sentence which describes how Sarah feels about David Hodgson.

   i)   Sarah hates David and tries to make life unpleasant for him.

   ii)   Sarah seems to feel sorry for David and tries to keep him happy.

   iii)   Sarah is madly in love with David and would do anything to make him happy.

Q2   Copy out two parts of the text that back up your answer.

Q3   For each of the three characters, pick out two words below that sum them up.

     arrogant   short-tempered   sympathetic   stressed   stunning   tolerant

Q4   For each of your choices in Q3, write down a phrase from the text that backs up your answer.

Q5   What do the words 'she tossed back her mane of honey-coloured hair' tell you about Denise?

There are three important bits in the phrase — 'tossed', 'mane' and 'honey-coloured'.

Q6   Why do you think the writer used the word 'sauntered' instead of 'walked'?

Q7   Describe the ways that the writer of *The Movie Murders* contrasts characters through descriptions. Use your answers to the questions on this page to help you.   (5 marks)

SAT-STYLE QUESTION

I'm ready for my close-up now...

<u>Always</u> remember to back up your points with evidence from the text. It's no good saying that 'Denise is a stuck-up old witch' if you can't prove it using the text. Even if it's true.

Similes and Metaphors

Writers often use comparisons to make their descriptions more vivid.
The two main types of comparison you need to know here, are similes and metaphors.

A gig review from a music newspaper

Any really great rock band knows that you have to keep your audience waiting. By the time The Strums arrived on stage, the audience were howling like wolves. Right from the start, singer Leo Ryder was a monster, roaring into the microphone. Guitarist Richie Z was possessed by the ghost of Jimi Hendrix as he played the most frantic guitar solos this side of Wigan. Jay Bryson beat the drums as if they were fires to be put out, but somehow managed to keep time as faithfully as an honest referee.

As soon as the band launched into their number 2 hit, 'The First Rule is...', the audience were like a seething wave of noise. If it wasn't already clear, this concert proves that The Strums are the heavyweight boxers of rock music — and they certainly don't pull any punches.

Q1   Write 'metaphor', 'simile' or 'neither' next to each of these phrases.

a)   you have to keep your audience waiting

b)   the audience were like a seething wave of noise

c)   The Strums are the heavyweight boxers of rock music

Similes say that something is like something else. Metaphors say that something is something else.

Q2   Which of these answers best explains why the writer describes the audience as 'howling like wolves'?

i)   The shouting audience sounded quiet and tuneful, like wolf howls.

ii)   The shouting audience sounded noisy and tuneless, like wolf howls.

iii)   The audience were eating raw meat and were very hairy.

Simile of the Day
A monkey's as much use to a vacuum cleaner as a vacuum cleaner is to a monkey.

Q3   Is the description in Q2 a simile or a metaphor?

Q4   Copy and complete the table showing the similes and metaphors that the writer uses.

Thing being described	Description the writer uses	Simile or metaphor	What this means
Leo Ryder			
Richie Z playing guitar			
Jay Bryson beating the drums			

Hello, I'm three — I've never metaphor before...

Fictional writing uses shiploads of metaphors and similes. They're imported from Greece, though some arrive on the black market to avoid customs tax. Learn to spot 'em. Also learn to spot bull.

Mood

Fiction writers build up the mood of a scene through the language they use. Basically, mood is about how the text <u>makes you feel</u> — whether it's happy, sad, funny, frightening, exciting...

A At last the waiting was over. Rachel held the exam results envelope and watched her friends opening theirs. Some smiled with relief, some stared at the floor.

Her fingers tugged gently at the envelope.

Slightly open now...

Nearly there...

B The mood took hold of the family like a virus. Mealtimes were now a matter of muttered greetings, lowered eyes and shared silences. Even the cracked ceilings had begun to weep rainwater. Gordon knew that Dexter had been *only* a dog, but he was missed like a member of the family.

C Katie strolled amid the laughing guests, her son Daniel trotting at her side. The sun caressed Katie's skin, while a cool breeze tickled the hair falling on her neck. The grass beneath her feet provided a soft carpet. Katie hadn't felt so alive in years.

Q1 Match up each of the texts A, B and C to one of the moods below.

tense   romantic   happy   horrific   funny   sad

Q2 In text A, is Rachel in a hurry to open the envelope? Use evidence from the extract to back up your answer.

Q3 Why do you think the writer of text B used the word "weep" instead of "let in"? Mention the overall mood of the text in your answer.

Q4 What does the word 'trotting' in text C tell you about how Daniel feels?

Q5 What effect do the short sentences at the end of text A have? Write out the correct answer.

i) They slow the pace down before Rachel opens the envelope, which builds up suspense.

ii) They speed the pace up after Rachel opens the envelope, which builds up suspense.

Q6 Which of the three texts would the sentence below fit into? Write a sentence to explain your answer.

Even in crowds people kept a respectful distance, turning their long, pale faces away.

Q7 Write a couple of sentences explaining what the phrase "muttered greetings, lowered eyes and shared silences" from text B tells you about the mood of the text.

Long Language Question

Time to try your hand at dealing with a longer text — the texts in the SATs will be at least
1 page long. Read the extract below and then have a go at answering the questions opposite.

This is an extract from the short story *The Sea Raiders* by H.G. Wells.

Mr Fison, torn by curiosity, began picking his way across the wave-worn rocks,
and, finding the wet seaweed that covered them thickly rendered* them extremely
slippery, he stopped, removed his shoes and socks, and coiled his trousers above his
knees. His object was, of course, merely to avoid stumbling into the rocky pools
about him, and perhaps he was rather glad, as all men are, of an excuse to resume,
even for a moment, the sensations of his boyhood. At any rate, it is to this, no
doubt, that he owes his life.

He approached his mark with all the assurance which the absolute security of this
country against all forms of animal life gives its inhabitants. The round bodies
moved to and fro, but it was only when he surmounted the skerry* of boulders I
have mentioned that he realised the horrible nature of the discovery. It came upon
him with some suddenness.

The rounded bodies fell apart as he came into sight over the ridge, and displayed
the pinkish object to be the partially devoured body of a human being, but whether
of a man or woman he was unable to say. And the rounded bodies were new and
ghastly looking creatures, in shape somewhat resembling an octopus, and with huge
and very long and flexible tentacles, coiled copiously on the ground. The skin had a
glistening texture, unpleasant to see, like shiny leather. The downward bend of the
tentacle-surrounded mouth, the curious excrescence* at the bend, the tentacles, and
the large intelligent eyes, gave the creatures a grotesque suggestion of a face. They
were the size of a fair-sized swine about the body, and the tentacles seemed to him
to be many feet in length. There were, he thinks, seven or eight at least of the
creatures. Twenty yards beyond them, amid the surf of the now returning tide, two
others were emerging from the sea.

Their bodies lay flatly on the rocks, and their eyes regarded him with evil interest;
but it does not appear that Mr Fison was afraid, or that he realised that he was in any
danger. Possibly his confidence is to be ascribed to the limpness of their attitudes.
But he was horrified, of course, and intensely excited and indignant at such
revolting creatures preying upon human flesh. He thought they had chanced upon a
drowned body. He shouted to them, with the idea of driving them off, and, finding
they did not budge, cast about him, picked up a big rounded lump of rock, and flung
it at one.

And then, slowly uncoiling their tentacles, they all began moving towards him —
creeping at first deliberately, and making a soft purring sound to each other.

rendered = *made*
skerry = *mound*
excrescence = *growth*

Long Language Question

OK, so maybe 'The Sea Raiders' is gruesome and bloodthirsty, but it's also chock-full of descriptions and other tricks that all good writers use. Answer these questions about it.

Q1 Read the third paragraph carefully and write out any phrases that describe what the creatures look like.

Q2 Quickly sketch a picture of one of the creatures, using descriptions from the third paragraph.

Q3 Write down which of the following words from the text are adjectives and which are adverbs.

i) wave-worn   ii) horrible   iii) ghastly   iv) copiously   v) flexible
vi) glistening   vii) flatly   viii) intensely   ix) revolting   x) slowly

Not sure what adjectives and adverbs are? Look them up and write out the definitions.

Q4 Which of the following extracts from the text contains a simile? Copy out the correct answer.

i)   And the rounded bodies were new and ghastly looking creatures...
ii)   The skin had a glistening texture, unpleasant to see, like shiny leather.
iii)   Their bodies lay flatly on the rocks, and their eyes regarded him with evil interest...
iv)   They were the size of a fair-sized swine...

Q5 Write out any words from the fourth paragraph of the extract that tell you about Mr Fison's reaction to the creatures.

Q6 Write out any parts of the text that give you the impression that the creatures are as intelligent as humans.

Q7 Write out any parts of the text that tell you about how the creatures move.

Q8 Which row of the table sums up how the creatures move and what effect the movement achieves?

	How the creatures move	Effect this achieves
i)	Very slowly	Makes the reader feel sad
ii)	Very quickly	Makes the text funnier
iii)	Very slowly	Builds up suspense
iv)	Very quickly	Builds up suspense

Q9 In the extract from *The Sea Raiders*, how does the writer convey the horror of the situation to the reader? Write half a page, using the questions on this page as prompts. (10 marks)

Convey the horror — eat the reader's face off...

Don't read the text just once — keep looking back at it when you're doing the questions. Pick out the bit of the text that the question refers to, and then read that bit again carefully.

Layout

Some of the texts that you get in the SATs will be laid out in a special way, e.g. with bullet points, headings or arrows. There are often questions about how the layout makes the information clearer. Look at the following three extracts and answer all the questions at the bottom of the page.

A

Tues 3rd Feb — Video camera finally arrived! Can't believe it took three weeks to get here.

Wed 4th Feb — Been playing with camera all day. Caroline came round and we wrote and filmed a pretend TV show. I got to be a game show host (naturally).

Thu 5th Feb — Dropped camera when I was trying to film myself on a skateboard — it doesn't look too healthy any more. Think I might take up photography instead.

B

Why go to the Lake District? It may not be the most 'happening' place, but there are often locally produced performances in Kendal, or specialist art films showing at the cinema.

What's in the local area? Well, most people go to the Lake District to walk in the hills. If you're less of an outdoor type, there are plenty of other diversions. The 'Theatre by the Lake' in Keswick is well worth a look.

Does anyone care about the Lake District? The Royal Shakespeare Company regularly tour Keswick and Kendal. The arts centre in Kendal is a member of the British Film Institute, so it often shows restored classic films.

C

Five tips for a healthy computer:

1. Always shut down the computer correctly after use.
2. Try not to have more than three applications running at once.   Using lots of programs at once will slow your computer down.
3. Always scan discs for viruses before you use them.   See next page for more on viruses.
4. Make sure your computer base unit is well ventilated.   Don't block the fan at the back of the unit, or it will overheat.
5. Don't eat or drink near your computer.

Q1   What kind of text do you think Extract A is taken from? Explain your answer.

Q2   Explain why it's important that the writer of Extract A included dates as subheadings.

Q3   Why are the subheadings in Extract B written as questions? Write out the best answer.

i)   To make the article feel like a speech read out by the writer.

ii)   To make the article feel like a conversation between the writer and the reader.

iii)   To annoy the reader and to make them feel stupid.

Q4   Why has the writer of Extract C numbered the five points?

Q5   Explain the purpose of the information in grey boxes in Extract C.

Q6   How do the arrows in Extract C help the reader to understand the text?

Structure

As well as layout, writers have to think about the order they put their information. You can get questions about this in the SATs, e.g. what makes a good introduction or conclusion.

A book review for a popular magazine

If asked about writer Alexis Bright, most people would react: "Who?" However, all this is about to change...

Bright's new novel, 'A Tale of Two Celebrities', is a vicious attack on the nature of celebrity in the 21st century. Set in present-day Manchester, it tells the story of the rivalry between failing TV host Richard and rising star Penelope.

The novel's fans (and there will be many) will applaud the author's bold statements and the unflinching satire of our obsession with celebrities. The book is sure to do brisk business, and is likely to be a big seller in airports and newsagents.

On the other hand, many people will scoff at the two-dimensional characters, as well as the unsatisfying ending (in which Richard and Penelope fight it out on air in a duel-like ratings war).

So, next time someone asks you about Alexis Bright, you'd better have read 'A Tale of Two Celebrities', so that you know where you stand.

Q1   Explain one way in which the first paragraph is effective as an introduction to the article.

Q2   Write a sentence to sum up what the writer tells you in the second paragraph.

Q3   Why do you think the writer put that paragraph straight after the introduction?

Q4   Sum up the differences between paragraphs 3 and 4, in one sentence.

Q5   Why do you think the writer put paragraphs 3 and 4 next to each other?

Q6   Write out the answer below that explains why the last sentence is a good ending to the text.

   i)   The last sentence refers back to the introduction and sums up the main point of the review.

   ii)   The last sentence makes a new point that is better than the other points in the text.

   iii) The last sentence tries to persuade the reader that 'A Tale of Two Celebrities' is terrible.

Q7   Explain how the writer structures the book review in a way that keeps the reader interested.
SAT-STYLE QUESTION   Write about half a page and use your answers to the above questions to help you.

(10 marks)

Structure — point don't I it of see the...

Writing needs to be well structured in order to get information across to the reader in a clear and logical way. The examiners think this is as important as regular teeth-brushing, so pay attention.

Persuading the Reader

Sometimes writers try to change the way the reader feels about something, whether it's in fiction or non-fiction. You need to know how to describe the tricks writers use to persuade you.

Questions 1 and 2 are about the advert for Bonza Biscuits below.

> **NEW! Bonza Biscuits!**
>
> *Bonza Biscuits* are the new luxury biscuit treat from Butler's Biscuit company. Not only are they tasty, they're great value too.
>
>
> Special introductory offer — only 70p per pack!
>
> Hurry to your local supermarket or Butler's Biscuits seller and demand your first packet of *Bonza Biscuits*. Introductory offer lasts 2 weeks only.
> *Bonza Biscuits* — the most satisfying chocolate biscuits you'll ever have.

Q1   What is the main aim of the advert?

Q2   Pick out all the phrases from the text that try to persuade the reader that Bonza Biscuits are great.

Watch out for words that <u>exaggerate</u> how wonderful the biscuits are.

Questions 3–5 are about the extract below.

> Looking at Mr Blister's face was like looking at a wet sponge wearing a hat. His narrow eyes squinted through his finger-printed spectacles, as if even looking at the idiots around him made him feel ill. He would often raise his pudgy, clay-like hand to rub his peeling nose or to wipe his damp forehead.
>
> Mr Blister bellowed instead of talking and he walked like a toad, moving in jumps and starts, taking long strides with his tree-trunk legs.

Q3   Copy out and fill in this table showing the descriptions of Mr Blister's body parts.

Body part	Description
legs	like tree trunks
forehead	
hands	
eyes	
nose	

You can just copy out the descriptions from the text for this question.

Q4   Write out the answer that is the best short description of Mr Blister.

i)   Mr Blister is a decent, good-looking man.

ii) Mr Blister is ugly but he's basically a nice person.

iii) Mr Blister is a really ugly and unpleasant man.

Q5   Write a short passage explaining whether or not you think the writer wants the reader to like Mr Blister. Use your answers to Q3 and Q4 to help you.   (3 marks)

SAT-STYLE QUESTION

Changes in the Writer's Opinion

Examiners love it if you spot when a writer's opinion changes during a text. So make the SATs examiners as happy as mice in a vat of cheese, and have a go at these questions.

> Extract from an article called *All The Fun of the Fair?*
>
> Ever since I've been very young I've been taken to circuses around the world. My parents saw it as an educational experience — and there was also the fact that I would get ridiculously excited at the sight of the animals on display. Lions, elephants, trained horses — all these animals prompted the same breathless response from me.
>
> In the years since then I've always retained a fondness for circuses despite the recent bad press — so naturally I was delighted to accept an offer to go backstage at Jackson's Travelling Circus.
>
> Unfortunately, the reality of the circus was far less exotic than I had previously believed. The lions in their cramped cages hardly resembled the proud hunters I'd imagined. The sight of the elephants pacing sadly up and down brought tears to my eyes. Even the beaming grins of the human performers were discarded once they'd left the ring.

Q1 Which of these phrases from the article <u>does not</u> show the writer's view of circuses as a child?

   i)   My parents saw it as an educational experience

   ii) I would get ridiculously excited at the sight of the animals on display

   iii) all these animals prompted the same breathless response from me

Q2 What happened to change the writer's opinion of circuses?

Q3 In which paragraph does the tone of the article become negative?

Q4 Write out a phrase from the text that signals this change of focus.

Q5 Write out a phrase from the text that shows the writer's emotions during the backstage tour.

Q6 Why did the writer add a question mark to the title of the article?
Explain why the answer below is wrong, and write out a better answer.

The writer added a question mark to the title 'All The Fun of the Fair?' to show that she used to believe that circuses were boring, but now she thinks that they're really exciting.

Q7 Write a short paragraph explaining why the writer's opinion changes during the extract. Use your answers to the questions on this page to help you.

SAT-STYLE QUESTION

(5 marks)

<u>Great page — no it's not — yes it is...</u>

Writers often give clues about their opinions in non-fiction texts — and mentioning if their opinions change will definitely get you buckets of extra marks. Which is better than a poke in the eye.

The Effect on the Reader

Writers try hard to get the reader involved in the story or argument.
You've got to keep your eyes peeled for ways that the reader will be affected by the text.

An extract from the book *I was a Member of the Barrow Gang*

> **OK**, just imagine the situation: an open safe, piles and piles of shining golden coins just waiting for me to get my hands on them — and surely you don't think I was unreasonable in assuming that my partners-in-crime had all been caught by now...
>
> I don't believe that there's a person in this world who would've done the decent thing and given themselves up to the police. Sure, I could have gone outside and tried to help out my partners, but you and I know that there would have been no point.
>
> **Well**, of course I took the money and ran. Wouldn't you?

Q1   Write a couple of sentences describing who the narrator is and what's happened.

Q2   Write out the phrase in the text that contains a rhetorical question.

Rhetorical questions are questions that don't need an answer.

Q3   What effect does the rhetorical question have on the reader? Write out the best answer.

   i)   It sounds as if the character is talking to himself.

   ii) It sounds as if the character is talking to you and it involves you in the decision.

   iii) It sounds as if the reader is asking the main character a question.

Q4   Write out the sentence below that explains why the writer chooses to include the phrase 'imagine the situation'.

   i)   The writer wants the reader to be the main character in the story.

   ii) The writer wants to stop the reader from identifying with the main character.

   iii) The writer wants to make the reader feel like they're actually taking part in the story.

Q5   Which of these phrases directly involves the reader in the story? Write out the correct phrases.

| piles and piles of shining golden coins | you and I know that there would have been no point | of course I took the money and ran | surely you don't think I was unreasonable |

Q6   How does the writer involve the reader in the story?
SAT-STYLE QUESTION
Use your answers to the questions on this page to help you.   (5 marks)

Check for split sides and wet pants...

Always show the examiner that you understand what the writing is trying to do. Even if you don't find something funny, it's worth saying if you think something is <u>supposed</u> to be funny.

Comparing Texts

Questions that ask you to compare different texts are sure to come up in the SATs.
Read through each of these texts, then turn the page and have a go at answering the questions.

A scientific account called *The Macaque Monkeys of Japan*

Day 1 — Macaque monkeys currently living in the centre of the island, within the forest area. Monkeys' day-to-day activities seem to be entirely according to accepted theories. Diet seems to be largely composed of berries.

Day 2 — Team placed large amount of potatoes in forest. May have to wait a while to see if the macaques show any interest.

Day 6 — It worked! Two days ago, the monkeys showed some interest in the potatoes — and since then they have made potatoes the main part of their diet. Team intends to move piles of potatoes closer to shore to see if the macaques follow.

Day 9 — Macaques definitely becoming comfortable with living on shoreline now, entirely depending on potatoes we supply. I even saw one monkey washing a potato in the sea before eating it! This development entirely unprecedented — seems to prove that monkeys are capable of dramatically changing their living patterns.

Day 11 — Macaques now entirely at home by shoreline. A few making effort to learn to swim in sea, and others starting to copy. Experiment declared a success — the macaques are learning afresh how to live their day-to-day life.

*Monkeys of the World Unite!
You have Nothing to Lose but your Bananas*

An extract from the novel *I, Monkey*

This is getting ridiculous. It was just a bit of fun letting the humans teach me sign language (and it really wasn't hard to learn) — but now they're excited and buzzing around like annoying flies. They've started saying that I'm the first ape to show real intelligence — the cheek of it! Just because we don't usually choose to humour their dreary experiments doesn't mean that we aren't capable of getting a message across.

Lots of people have come to visit since I started answering back through sign language. Most of them are pretty sad specimens with faces as pale as their white coats. I was going to give them a nice surprise by saying a few words, maybe have a chat about the weather — but it's getting boring now, so I think I might just be on my way.

instinct = in-built patterns of behaviour in response to certain things

---

An extract from an article called *Monkey Behaviour*

Humans may learn a lot from insects and animals. Humans will always question what they're doing and why they're doing it — but, for instance, a worker bee will always know its role in the beehive. It may feed the young or guard the hive, but it will always carry out its duty without even needing to be told. The same is true of more 'intelligent' organisms, such as the monkey. Although monkeys can be taught tricks (even to the extent of appearing to relish drinking tea in TV adverts), they are not able to break out of the simple instinctive pattern which instructs them exactly how to live their lives.

Too right. Down with this sort of thing.

Comparing Texts

Keep turning the page to check the texts when you're doing these questions. In the SATs you'll probably only have to compare two texts, but I've given you three for extra practice.

Q1 Match up each text to its description.

The Macaque Monkeys of Japan		Story
I, Monkey		Magazine article
Monkey Behaviour		Diary

Q2 Write out a phrase from *I, Monkey* that contains a simile.

Q3 Write out a phrase from *I, Monkey* that uses humour.

Q4 Write out a sentence from *The Macaque Monkeys of Japan* that is written in informal language.

Q5 Why do you think the writer of *The Macaque Monkeys of Japan* decided to break up the text into sections?

Q6 Which of these phrases from *The Macaque Monkeys of Japan* gives a fact rather than an opinion?

i) Macaque monkeys currently living in the centre of the island

ii) seems to prove that monkeys are capable of dramatically changing their living patterns

iii) the macaques are learning afresh how to live their day-to-day life

Q7 Write out the paragraph that sums up what happens in the extract from *I, Monkey*.

i) The scientists believe that monkeys are only capable of learning very basic sign language. The scientists are clever, so they are probably right.

ii) The monkey is more intelligent than the scientists realise. The monkey tells the story from his point of view, which shows the scientists are wrong.

Q8 Write out the paragraph that sums up the writer's opinion in *Monkey Behaviour*.

i) The writer thinks that humans are not ruled by instinct, but that all animals and insects are.

ii) The writer thinks that humans are ruled by instinct, but animals and insects are not.

iii) The writer thinks that all animals, including humans, are completely ruled by instinct.

Comparing Texts

Now you can move on to the longer comparing questions. When you're comparing two texts, make sure you don't write too much on one — write an equal amount for each text.

Q9   Write out the sentence that best describes the main idea in <u>all three texts</u>.

   i)   All three texts are about whether monkeys can instinctively talk.

   ii) All three texts are about whether the behaviour of monkeys is purely instinctive.

   iii) All three texts are about whether monkeys know that their behaviour is instinctive.

Q10 Copy and complete this table comparing all three texts.
     Use your answers to the questions on the previous page to help you.

Name of extract	The Macaque Monkeys of Japan	I, Monkey	Monkey Behaviour
Is the extract fiction or non-fiction?			
Is descriptive language used?			
Is the language formal or informal?			
Is there a first-person narrator?			
Does the writer use facts to back up their points?			
Does the writer think that animals are ruled by instinct?			

Now make use of your answers so far to answer the next three questions.
The table above is going to be especially useful.

Q11 **SAT-STYLE QUESTION** Re-read *The Macaque Monkeys of Japan* and *I, Monkey*. Write a short description of the differences between the layout and structure of each of the texts.   (3 marks)

Q12 **SAT-STYLE QUESTION** Re-read *I, Monkey* and *Monkey Behaviour*. Write a paragraph describing the differences between the language used in each of the texts.   (3 mark

Q13 **SAT-STYLE QUESTION** Re-read *The Macaque Monkeys of Japan* and *Monkey Behaviour*. Write a paragraph describing the differences between the writers' opinions about animal instinct.   (3 ma

"Romeo & Julie" — "do I get my banana now?" (monkey 5

Questions 11-13 on this page are like the ones you'll get in the SATs. Don't forget that you sh
write the same amount on both of the texts you're comparing, if you want to get good mar

Answers Without Prompts

Sometimes those mean SATs examiners give you questions without any hints at all.
You should always write out a list of prompts to remind you of the things you need to mention
in your answer. When you've read the text on the flap have a go at these questions.

Q1   Here's a question with no prompts at all. Copy out and correct the answer to the question.

> Explain how Oscar Wilde's use of similes and metaphors conveys Dorian's state of mind in the extract.

Hint: There are two errors in the answer.

Wilde writes that "a sharp pang of pain struck like a knife across him", and this metaphor shows that Dorian feels physically hurt when he realises that he will grow old. Later, Dorian calms down again when Wilde writes that "he felt as if a hand of ice had been laid upon his heart".

Q2   Write out the group of three prompts that would help you to answer the question below.

> Comment on the way that Lord Henry and Basil Hallward act towards Dorian Gray.

- *How does Hallward feel about Lord Henry?*
- *How does Lord Henry react to Hallward?*
- *How does Dorian feel about the painting?*

- *How does Hallward feel about his painting?*
- *How does Lord Henry react to seeing the painting?*
- *What do the characters say to Dorian before and after seeing the painting?*

Q3   Explain why the group of three prompts that you <u>didn't</u> pick would be unsuitable.

Q4   Write out three of the prompts in grey boxes that would help you answer the question below.

> Comment on the effectiveness of the language used to describe old age in the extract.

- *How does the language make the reader feel about old age?*
- *What does panegyric mean?*
- *What is Lord Henry's opinion about old age?*
- *What happens to make Dorian change his opinion of old age?*
- *Which phrases describe Dorian's body when he is old?*
- *Does Oscar Wilde use similes and metaphors in the extract?*

Write a list of three prompts that would help you answer the question below.

What is Dorian Gray's opinion of old age by the end of the extract?

Answers Without Prompts

The two pages of questions are about breaking long questions down into smaller pieces.
Read the extract below and then have a go at the questions, referring back whenever you need to.

This is an extract from the novel *The Picture of Dorian Gray* by Oscar Wilde.

After about a quarter of an hour, Hallward stopped painting, looked for a long time at Dorian Gray, and then for a long time at the picture, biting the end of one of his huge brushes, and smiling. "It is quite finished," he cried, at last, and stooping down he wrote his name in thin vermilion letters on the left-hand corner of the canvas.

Lord Henry came over and examined the picture. It was certainly a wonderful work of art, and a wonderful likeness as well.

"My dear fellow, I congratulate you most warmly," he said.—"Mr. Gray, come and look at yourself."

The lad started, as if awakened from some dream. "Is it really finished?" he murmured, stepping down from the platform.

"Quite finished," said Hallward. "And you have sat splendidly to-day. I am awfully obliged to you."

"That is entirely due to me," broke in Lord Henry. "Isn't it, Mr. Gray?"

Dorian made no answer, but passed listlessly in front of his picture and turned towards it. When he saw it he drew back, and his cheeks flushed for a moment with pleasure. A look of joy came into his eyes, as if he had recognized himself for the first time. He stood there motionless, and in wonder, dimly conscious that Hallward was speaking to him, but not catching the meaning of his words. The sense of his own beauty came on him like a revelation. He had never felt it before. Basil Hallward's compliments had seemed to him to be merely the charming exaggerations of friendship. He had listened to them, laughed at them, forgotten them. They had not influenced his nature. Then had come Lord Henry, with his strange panegyric on youth, his terrible warning of its brevity. That had stirred him at the time, and now, as he stood gazing at the shadow of his own loveliness, the full reality of the description flashed across him. Yes, there would be a day when his face would be wrinkled and wizen, his eyes dim and colourless, the grace of his figure broken and deformed. The scarlet would pass away from his lips, and the gold steal from his hair. The life that was to make his soul would mar his body. He would become ignoble, hideous, and uncouth.

As he thought of it, a sharp pang of pain struck like a knife across him, and made each delicate fibre of his nature quiver. His eyes deepened into amethyst, and a mist of tears came across them.

He felt as if a hand of ice had been laid upon his heart.

"Don't you like it?" cried Hallward at last, stung a little by the lad's silence, and not understanding what it meant.

"Of course he likes it," said Lord Henry. "Who wouldn't like it? It is one of the greatest things in modern art. I will give you anything you like to ask for it. I must have it."

"It is not my property, Harry."

"Whose property is it?"

"Dorian's, of course."

"He is a very lucky fellow."

> panegyric = a speech
> in praise of something

"How sad it is!" murmured Dorian Gray, with his eyes still fixed upon his own portrait. "How sad it is! I shall grow old, and horrid, and dreadful. But this picture will remain always young. It will never be older than this particular day of June. . . . If it was only the other way! If it was I who were to be always young, and the picture that were to grow old! For this—for this—I would give everything! Yes, there is nothing in the whole world I would not give!"

FOLD THIS PAGE OUT
*Read the text, then do the
questions on the following pages.*

Answers Without Prompts

Another page about how to deal with long, murderous questions which give you no hints at all. [N.B. You can also try leaving the country and buying a house in Rio.]

Q6 Write out the sentence that sums up Dorian's view of himself at the <u>start</u> of the extract.

   i) Dorian isn't really aware of his beauty and doesn't believe the nice things that people say.

   ii) Dorian knows he is beautiful and loves hearing people say nice things about him.

   iii) Dorian is vain and wants everyone to see his beautiful portrait.

Q7 Copy out phrases from the text that back up your answer to Q6.

Q8 What happens in the text to make Dorian change his opinion of himself?

Q9 How does Dorian feel about his appearance afterwards? Write out the correct answer.

   i) Dorian realises that he is not as beautiful as he thought beforehand.

   ii) Dorian realises that he is as beautiful as people have been telling him.

   iii) Dorian wishes that he was even more beautiful that he already is.

...because I'm worth it.

Q10 Copy out a phrase from the text that backs up your answer to Q9.

Hint: There are two errors in the answer.

Q11 How does Dorian feel about growing old? Copy and correct this answer.

Dorian imagines when his face is 'wrinkled and wizen' and he feels so horrified that the thought hurts 'like a sword across him'. He imagines when 'the scarlet would pass away from his lips', which shows that he thinks that he will become mean as well as ugly.

Q12 What does Dorian wish for at the end of the extract? What does this tell you about his feelings?

Q13 Use questions 6-12 to write a list of prompts to answer the question at the bottom of the page.

Q14 Now answer this SAT-style question. Your prompts and answers from all the other questions on this page should help loads.

SAT-STYLE QUESTION

> How does Dorian Gray's opinion of himself change during the extract?   (5 marks)

Born to be Wilde...

Phew... now you've done these pages you'll be able to break down long questions into manageable chunks, bung them on cocktail sticks and eat 'em like pineapple.

Proper SAT Reading Questions

Now it's high time that you put all the skills together to tackle some real(ish) SATs questions.
When you've read the article on the left have a go at these short questions.

Q1   Which country hosted the first World Cup?   (1 mark)

Q2   Copy and complete the table below showing facts from the extract.   (3 marks)

Description of fact	Number
Year of first World Cup final	
Largest stadium audience	
Year Football Association was created	
Total viewing figures of 1998 World Cup	
Year Charles Miller took football to Brazil	
Number of teams playing in first World Cup Final	
Year World Cup match sparked a war	

Q3   Write down the first country to play football on record, and how long ago that was.   (1 mark)

Q4   Write down the two countries involved in a war sparked off by a World Cup match.   (1 mark)

Q5   Who originally thought up the idea of the World Cup?   (1 mark)

Q6   Where was the World Cup created?   (1 mark)

Q7   Why do you think the writer says that "the history of football goes back <u>ever so slightly</u> further than 1930"?   (2 marks)

Q8   Why do you think the writer used the phrase "snarling like hyenas" to describe the football fans in the first paragraph?   (2 marks)

Q9   Why do you think the writer uses the phrase "bloody, sweaty battlefield" at the end of the third paragraph?   (2 marks)

Q10   Explain why the writer numbered the points in the section "What's so great about football?".   (2 marks)

Q11   Why do you think the writer uses questions for the subheadings?   (2 marks)

KEEP TURNING

Proper SAT Reading Questions

You know the drill — read the text carefully, have a go at the questions, refer back to this text whenever you need to. Except this time there are loads more questions, and they're trickier too.

This is an extract from a magazine article called *World Cup Fever*.

A shrill blast. The 'thunk' of leather against leather. The air is filled with the sounds of shouting and stamping feet. Thousands of people with brightly painted faces are snarling like hyenas at their opponents. No, this is not a scene from the film *Braveheart*. It's even more serious — it's the World Cup.

The World Cup was thought up by Jules Rimet in Paris, and the first Final was in 1930. The host, Uruguay, offered to pay for travel expenses for the other teams. They were rewarded by winning, and declared a national day of holiday. Mind you, there were only 13 teams playing!

Where did football come from?

The history of football goes back ever so slightly further than 1930. The first records of the game were about 5000 years ago in China. Versions of football were also played by the ancient Greeks, Egyptians, and Romans. In the 16th century in Italy, a similar game called *calcio* was played, with a decapitated head used for the ball! In Britain we weren't much more humane either. Imagine the scene in medieval England: it's a national holiday and virtually every town in the country is turned into a bloody, sweaty battlefield that only faintly resembles a football pitch.

Later on, the British claimed the game as their own, before introducing it to countries around the world. In 1894 Charles Miller changed the face of Brazil for good when he left his boat carrying a football in each hand. Now most people recognise Brazil as the home of the most beautifully played football in the world.

The modern rules of football were only made concrete in 1963 when the Football Association was founded – and the game has evolved into the one we know and love today.

Is it _really_ the beautiful game?

So, the modern game of football has inspired and entertained people for decades, but it hasn't all been good. We're all aware of the phenomenon of football hooliganism. Although more and more regulations are being brought in to prevent them, these idiots continue to spoil the game for many other people. However, football has been indirectly responsible for even worse things. In 1969 a controversial World Cup qualifying match between El Salvador and Honduras contributed to war breaking out between the two countries!

Proper SAT Reading Questions

What's so great about football?

Football is amazingly popular around the world. The largest stadium audience for a game was in Rio de Janeiro for the 1950 World Cup Final, when 200,000 people turned up to see the game. Nowadays, matches are transmitted live to the whole world on TV. The total viewing figures for the whole of the 1998 World Cup were 33.4 billion people from 196 countries — and there's only 6 billion people in the world, so everyone must have watched lots of different matches!

There are many ideas about why football is so popular around the world:

1) *The basic rules are very simple – they don't need much explanation and so people can play football without even being able to talk the same language.*

2) *It doesn't take much organisation – all you need is a ball, a flat space of land and some markers for goalposts.*

3) *There's the potential for real drama – the game is very physical, and footballers can show off their skills.*

Who are the biggest football fans?

During World Cup season in Brazil, walls and lamp-posts are often painted in the national team colours of green and yellow. In Britain we might not be quite as dramatic, but in 2002 we once again proved our devotion to football when thousands of people made excuses to miss school or work in order to watch the World Cup games held in South Korea and Japan. Even those of us who wouldn't normally watch football managed to get caught up in the national excitement, including me...

...but I still don't understand the offside rule.

FOLD THIS PAGE OUT

*Read the text, then do the
questions on the following pages.*

Proper SAT Reading Questions

Thinking that the last page was a bit of a doddle? This one's full of longer SAT-style questions.
Remember that it's often useful to break long questions down into smaller chunks.

Q12   Explain one way in which the first paragraph is effective as an introduction to the article. Use phrases from the text to back up your answer.   (3 marks)

Q13   Copy and complete the table, by summing up each subsection in one sentence.   (3 marks)

Subsection	Summary
Introduction	
'Where did football come from?'	
'Is it really the beautiful game?'	
'What's so great about football?'	
'Who are the biggest football fans?'	

Q14   Sum up the whole article in no more than three sentences.   (2 marks)

Q15   The section "Is it *really* the beautiful game?" is more negative than the rest of the text. Write out one phrase from this section that tells you the writer's opinion.   (2 marks)

Q16   Explain what Charles Miller did to "change the face of Brazil".   (2 marks)

Q17   The article begins: "A shrill blast. The 'thunk' of leather against leather." Explain what the writer is referring to in these two sentences.   (2 marks)

Q18   Using facts from the text, give three reasons why football is extremely popular.   (2 marks)

Q19   Do you think the final sentence is a good ending to the text? Back up your answer with phrases from the text.   (5 marks)

Q20   Sum up the writer's opinion of football, using evidence from the whole text to back up your answer.   (5 marks)

Q21   How does the writer use humour to keep the reader interested? Use phrases from the text to back up your answer.   (5 marks)

Q22   In the whole article, explain how the writer presents the history of football as both positive and surprisingly violent.   (5 marks)

Stressful And Tiring (anonymous quote)

In the SAT there'll be about five questions per text. I've given you millions of questions about the text because I'm just generous with giving you practice. If I say so myself. Oh, now I'm blushing.

Sentences, Phrases and Clauses

Use language correctly and the SAT examiners will reward you with a pile of juicy marks. Grammar's here to haunt you until the end of your days — so get it sorted.

Q1 Read parts a)-i). Write down why each one <u>isn't</u> a proper sentence.

a) The dog walked slowly up the drive, regretting the mess he'd made of the roses

b) the wind in my hair.

c) Paul said that he liked Vienna

d) The Romans' legendary cruelty to Octavia.

e) Wanted a headlamp for his car.

f) she wants to go but her father thinks it's a silly idea

g) Before the winter.

h) Ran to the shops.

i) Bananas for £2.20 a kilo.

Psst — you ain't seen me, right?

Q2 Write down whether a)-i) are phrases, clauses or main clauses.

phrase = a group of words without a verb

clause = a group of words with a verb

main clause = a clause which makes sense on its own and could be a sentence

a) the hedgehog's evil spikes

b) spitting in the fish tank

c) we went to Olivia Newton-John's house

d) running to the river

e) on the way to the bus

f) Rita Hayworth is gorgeous

g) in the autumn

h) William paused thoughtfully

i) despite the heavy rain

verb = a 'doing' or 'being' word

Q3 Match up the phrases and the clauses below. Write them out as sentences, putting a comma between the phrase and the clause.

Phrases

a) Before the start of term

b) In the Atlantic ocean

c) In his best Western movies

d) Without a bit of mustard

e) Without a doubt

f) Very well then

g) In a desperate attempt at humour

h) Up in the attic

Clauses

1) you can see fish swimming

2) this recipe tastes disgusting

3) my brother tried to poison a rat

4) porridge is better than gruel

5) I'll fight you for it

6) Gary Cooper's acting was impressive

7) Kim threw the egg against the wall

8) I'll have to cram in lots of fun

Commas, Semicolons and Colons

Commas, semi-colons and colons are all used to break sentences up into manageable chunks. Try pausing slightly where you want to put the comma, etc. to see if it sounds right.

Q1 Copy out the following sentences, adding commas, to make the meaning clearer.

a) Walking beside the miniature poodle Harley felt very tall indeed.

b) Helen pitied the spider in the sink which was about to die.

c) Scurrying out of the way of the headmistress Dana looked a bit sheepish.

d) He walked and talked half an hour afterwards his head was cut off.

Q2 Copy out the sentences, adding commas to separate the clauses and phrases.

e.g. Though a good singer Frank Sinatra was a naughty man in real life.
Though a good singer, Frank Sinatra was a naughty man in real life.

phrase   clause

a) After the storm was over my sister returned to the ranch.

b) Despite everything I still had a soft spot for her.

c) He marched away from the station without a single look back.

d) Way back many centuries ago not long after the Bible began Jacob lived in the land of Canaan a fine example of a family man.

e) Although the weather was hot Abigail decided to wear a big jumper and corduroy trousers.

Q3 All these sentences have colons missing. Copy out the sentences, adding colons in the right place.

Colons are used: 1) before lists, 2) before a long quotation, 3) before an explanation.

a) I'll tell you how I managed it I walked up to him and asked him.

b) All I want from my hamster is companionship, devotion and a small but tasty meal.

c) As my grandmother says "Don't fight with your Grandad or I'll get you."

d) You should bring the following things an inflatable dinghy, a life jacket and a foghorn.

e) Pigeons have been known to communicate as follows "eeuak, eak, ouawk, ek-ek, ooch."

Q4 The following sentences have semicolons in the wrong place. Copy out the sentences, moving the semicolons to the right places.

a) The star required: a trailer with a jacuzzi three servants; including a manicurist a separate dog kennel and; Scottish salmon sandwiches without crusts.

b) The footballer had it all: a strong left foot a good eye; for the ball a lightning pace; and nerves of steel.

Semi-colons are used to join together linked sentences, and to break up lists when the items are quite long.

c) He walked; into the room he had never been inside before.

d) Jim had made a huge pile he owned; a large percentage of the Nile.

Apostrophes

Teachers love complaining that 'young people these days' don't know how to use apostrophes.
Do this page and you'll be able to knock them sideways with your stunning apostrophe know-how.

Q1   Read the following sentences a)-g). Copy down the sentences where <u>it's</u>, <u>its</u>, <u>there's</u> and <u>theirs</u> are wrong and change them so they're right.

a)   Our son might not be perfect, but their's is atrocious.

b)   Theres a small cat which lives in our barn.

c)   Its sunny outside — why stay indoors?

d)   The driver wanted the car repaired because its' gearbox was making funny noises.

e)   I really like the theatre; theirs a good one in my home town.

f)   It's hardly surprising that no children like Blue Peter: all their parents do.

g)   "Its a Wonderful Life" is a film with Jimmy Stewart. Its shown every Christmas.

Q2   Apostrophes are used to show that something belongs.
Copy out the sentences below, putting apostrophes in the right places.

> e.g.   Philippas cows were a bit special.
> *Philippa's cows were a bit special.*

a)   The ostriches beaks were all shiny.

b)   My brother Alexs band are playing in the pub on Saturday.

c)   She gave him her mums favourite handkerchief, realising too late that it was covered in snot.

d)   The childrens section of the menu was uninspiring.

e)   Elmer McCurdys body was used as a fairground attraction for seventy years
before people realised it was human and gave him a proper burial.

f)   Marcus piano was six feet tall; he couldn't reach the pedals.

Q3   In informal writing, it's usual to combine or shorten certain words as if you were
speaking. Copy the sentences below, combining or shortening the highlighted words.

a)   I do not want to trouble you, but your Alsatian is in my garage.

b)   The boxer will not fight without his lucky rabbit's foot.

c)   Do you not think it's strange how television stars get thinner every year?

d)   It is the best piece of music I have ever heard.

e)   It is not that unusual for people to have two part-time jobs.

f)   I cannot go to the gym. I will not go to the gym.
I do not want to go to the gym.

> *Apostrophes are used to show that letters are missing.*

Honestly, she's just shy because you're here.

FYI — Philippa's cows could dance like Fred Astaire...

It was like a really bad cheese advert — they looked all knock-kneed and cow-like but then suddenly
they were off, foxtrotting across the field. [Well, you think of summat interesting to say about apostrophes.]

Speech, Question and Exclamation Marks

"A page on speech and question marks?" I said. "Oh, and exclamation marks. No problem!"

Q1 Decide whether each of the following sentences needs to include speech marks.
Copy out the ones which do, adding speech marks in the right places.

a) When asked if he was a communist, Ring Lardner Jr. replied
I could tell you but I would hate myself in the morning.

b) Mae West used to quip that when she was good she
was very good but when she was bad she was better.

Remember to add the right punctuation and capital letters to the sentences too.

c) Bette Davis said the famous line fasten your seat belts,
it's going to be a bumpy night in the film 'All About Eve'.

d) When Tony Blair got into power, he kept saying education,
education, education.

e) Franz Fanon said that the revolutionaries wanted Algeria to be a place
open to all, where any kind of genius could grow.

Q2 Read the following passage. Copy it out, putting in two question marks and three exclamation
marks in appropriate places. You may need to make the odd letter capital too.

> Jake burst through the door of the garage shop.
> "Freeze" he shouted. He was scared; he could feel the sweat rolling
> down his forehead and flooding his eyes. He moved towards the cashier,
> holding the bag out in one hand, grasping his fake gun in the other.
> "Oh my life" said the cashier, "Jake Smithson, what are you doing"
> Jake stopped in his tracks. He had been told that a pair of tights over the
> head would render any human being unrecognisable. Maybe 15 denier
> wasn't enough.
> "I'm not Jake Smithson," he said, backing away.
> "Yes you are, I used to serve you lunch at St Hilda's Primary School.
> Fancy that what are you getting up to these days" she said. Quietly, she
> pressed the police alarm under the counter.

Q3 Copy out the following sentences, adding correct punctuation (including speech marks).

a) I'm hard to get said Slim all you have to do is ask.

b) My name is Maximus Decimus Meridus said the stranger and I will
have my vengeance in this life or the next.

c) I think I'm falling in love with her said Fritz. Oh, I am sorry said Brian.
So am I said Fritz.

d) She was awfully decent about that cheese said Caldicott.
But I see she didn't leave much of the pickles said Charters.

e) I demand that you pay me one million dollars said Dr. Evil.

f) You say you're alone but your table's set for four said the policeman.
That's nothing the man replied my alarm clock's set for eight.

Optional question: match the quotes with the films —
i) Cabaret
ii) To Have and Have Not
iii) A Night at the Opera
iv) Austin Powers
v) The Lady Vanishes
vi) Gladiator

Writing Interesting Sentences

Always vary the types of sentences you use, to keep the reader interested. That means making some sentences short and some long, and using tricks like rhetorical questions. Geddit?

Q1   Write these sentences out with a connecting word that joins together the two clauses.

a)   Jim ran to the station .... he needed to catch the last train.

b)   I am prepared to wait .... the governor decides what will happen.

c)   Sergei Bubka thinks he is the best pole-vaulter in the world .... I am better.

d)   I was about to go shopping .... the letter landed on the mat.

e)   My ceramic frog collection is terrific .... it's worth a lot of money too.

Q2   Copy out each of these sentences, splitting each one into two shorter sentences.
You may need to remove a few words from some for the new sentence to make sense.

a)   Isabel had only got one ticket and she didn't want to give it away.

b)   Pancakes with sugar and lemon are good but jam filling is also nice.

c)   Daria flew over the wall and landed in a heap at the bottom of the ditch.

d)   St Malo is really hot in the summer so you can go swimming in the sea.

e)   Una was going to miss the plane unless she could grab a lift on the boy's skateboard.

Q3   Rewrite these sentences as rhetorical questions.

    e.g.   Christopher panicked; it was possible the vile mice had eaten the food.
                Christopher panicked; surely the vile mice hadn't eaten the food?

a)   We all know that paint dries very slowly.

b)   We don't need to ask whether the governor will be back next year.

c)   You seem to be saying that Muriel is lying, but that's ridiculous.

d)   Cybil didn't know where to look; she thought that man had left five days ago.

Q4   The following paragraph is badly written. Make it sound better by making some sentences shorter and others longer — do it by splitting or combining sentences.

> Rita Hayworth was born in 1918. She was born in America. Her original name was Margarita Cansino. Her family were Spanish. From the age of 13 she danced in a stage act with her father. She spent a lot of time practising her dancing. This meant she missed out on most of her education. In the late 1930s, she started to get small roles in films, but the American film industry was xenophobic and therefore didn't like the fact that she looked Spanish so her appearance was changed in the following ways: her black hair was dyed red and her hairline was made higher by electrolysis; in addition to this her Spanish-sounding name was changed to Rita Hayworth.

Writing Interesting Sentences

Easy tricks to make your writing more readable are: 1) vary how you start sentences, 2) vary the verbs you use, and 3) use pronouns when you can.

If you're not sure about verbs and pronouns, take a look at the CGP 'Essential Terms' book.

Q1 Swap the phrases and clauses of the following sentences around, so that they don't start with 'I'.

a) I dashed to the supermarket, even though it was raining.

b) I had to stop running; it didn't matter if the police caught me any more.

c) I will go on a fantastic holiday to Iceland, in the autumn.

d) I said, "Please go away."

e) I opened the satchel, suddenly worried.

Q2 Write down a more interesting verb which you could use instead of 'went' in each sentence.

a) Hayley went to the museum in her new car.

b) Mahmoud went to the box office, hoping he'd be in time to get a ticket.

c) Despite all the fuss she had made, Janice went in the aeroplane in the end.

d) Becky went around the shops after her gran, wishing she wasn't there.

e) The lamb went along the grass, looking very cute.

Q3 Write down a pronoun which could be used instead of the highlighted words in the following sentences.

Pronouns are words which stand in for a noun. They include: I, you, he, she, it, we, they, mine, yours, us, them.

e.g. Barnaby loved the smell of nachos. Barnaby also loved cricket.
Barnaby loved the smell of nachos. He also loved cricket.

a) I had hated Steve ever since Steve fouled me in football by dragging his studs down my leg.

b) The Five Nations tournament is on next week. I always watch the Five Nations on TV.

c) This is the biggest My Little Pony collection in the world. The My Little Ponies are all mine.

d) Sonia waited for Ahmed to finish work, then Sonia walked with Ahmed to the park.

e) Pete Postlethwaite is my sister's favourite actor. My sister really likes Pete Postlethwaite.

Q4 Rewrite these paragraphs. Replace some of the repeated nouns with pronouns to make it sound *slick*.

Hint: you can replace place names with the pronoun 'there'

Franz Fanon was born in the French colony of Martinique. Franz Fanon trained as a psychologist in France. Franz Fanon encountered racism in France. Franz Fanon then decided to move to Algeria, which was a French colony. During his time in Algeria, Franz Fanon worked at a hospital.

Franz Fanon supported the Algerian revolution against French colonial rule which started in 1954. The Algerian revolution was very bitter and violent. In his role as a psychologist, Franz Fanon treated both French soldiers who had tortured Algerian revolutionaries, and the victims of torture. Franz Fanon wrote a book about the revolution, called 'A Dying Colonialism'. The book is very good.

Writing Interesting Sentences

Variety is the key to writing interesting sentences. Variety is the key to writing interesting sentences.
Variety is the key to writing interesting sentences. Variety is the key to writing interesting sentences.

Q1 Active sentences make writing more interesting and engaging.
For each pair of sentences below, write down which is passive and which is active.

a) The hamster ate a large plate of fish and chips.

i) A large plate of fish and chips was eaten by the hamster.

b) Smoking is not allowed in the igloos.
ii) You shouldn't smoke in the igloos.

c) Reginald visited Buckingham Palace.
iii) Buckingham Palace was visited by Reginald.

d) A plate of spaghetti was thrown over the dog by Lisa.
iv) Lisa threw a plate of spaghetti over the dog.

Q2 Direct commands tell the reader exactly what to do.
Rewrite the following sentences, making them into direct commands.

Example: You should be wary of the ferocious chipmunks of Honolulu.
Beware the ferocious chipmunks of Honolulu.

a) I think you should keep quiet in the museum.

b) Maybe you shouldn't smoke in the flammable wigwam.

c) Why not try eating the frosted peas?

d) Why don't you go down to the dock of the bay?

Q3 You need to make sure that you write exactly what you mean. Copy out
this table and fill in the blanks with phrases from the box below.

Don't spend ages drawing the table — it doesn't have to be a work of art.

What Leo said to John in the pub last night	How likely is it that Leo will buy the beer?
"I should buy some of your homemade beer."	
"I might buy some of your homemade beer."	
"If I was richer, I would buy your homemade beer."	
"I will buy some of your homemade beer."	
"I can buy your homemade beer."	

he'll definitely buy the beer
he won't buy the beer
he feels he ought to buy it, but it isn't definite that he will
he is able to buy it, but it isn't definite that he will
it's possible he will buy the beer

Vocabulary

Make an effort to use nice vocabulary. Oops. Make an effort to use vampish, varied and vivacious vocabulary. It gets you marks. What more do you want from life? Well, apart from...

> Nice car
> like a Z3
> Direct a film
> by age of 20
> World record
> for high wages
> Retire young

Q1 Identify the nouns in the following sentences.
Then copy out the sentences, adding an adjective to all of the nouns.

e.g. The (man) was happy because he'd bought a (painting.)
> _The <u>rich</u> man was happy because he'd bought a <u>beautiful</u> painting._

a)   The boy was scared that the dog would attack him.

b)   Swimming is exercise.

A noun is a thing (e.g. a person, place or object). An adjective is a word that describes a noun.

c)   Orpheus knew that he shouldn't look, but the temptation to see his wife was too much.

d)   A wave came towards the shore and drenched the sunbathers.

e)   In the park near my house there is an oak tree.

f)   I didn't know until that moment how I would cope in such a situation.

g)   It was three days before they realised that the hamster had escaped.

h)   "It is a fact that Robert Mitchum is an actor," said my mum.

a verb is a 'doing' or 'being' word

Q2 Write out the sentence below with each of the endings a)-e). Change the verb "said" to a more interesting verb each time. Choose from the verbs in the grey box below.

Maria turned to Emma and <u>said,</u>

> whispered
> bellowed
> groaned
> griped
> warbled

a) "I think we should be quiet; no one else is talking in here."

b) "Get out of my sight, you ungrateful, horrible woman."

c) "The hills are alive with the sound of music."

d) "Not another gas bill."

e) "All the other waitresses get better tips than me."

Q3 Copy out these sentences, putting an adverb with each verb.

adverbs are words which describe a verb

e.g. The spy (walked) over to the desk.

> **The spy walked <u>calmly</u> over to the desk. OR <u>Calmly</u>, the spy walked over to the desk.**

a)   Jane welcomed the professor.

b)   The captain shouted at his daughter.

c)   I walked down to the riverbank.

d)   The cat eyed the salmon.

e)   "Surely not the Maltese Falcon?" said Sam.

f)   The robber was caught in the street.

g)   The mastermind paced up and down the dank room.

Nope, it's the Falcon's Malteser.

Writing — Grammar, Vocabulary and Spelling

Vocabulary

Always think about who you're writing for. If you're writing an imaginative story it might be OK to use all sorts of wacky words — but if you're writing a formal letter, you can't.

Q1 Copy and complete the table. For each underlined word think of two more words which have a similar meaning — one formal, one informal.

	The girl was <u>nice</u>.	The play was <u>interesting</u>.	The results were <u>bad</u>.	She's <u>good</u> at the piano.	The sea captain was <u>old</u>.
informal word	friendly				
formal word	pleasant				

Q2 Read this extract from a letter.

> The pigeons, which invaded the church steeple two months ago, are really annoying. For starters, they squawk all the time so you can't hear yourself think, let alone hear the First Soprano. Plus, we have to put up with bird poo in the choir stalls. It really is too much to bear.

a) Write down any words and phrases which would be too informal if you were writing to an MP.

b) Rewrite the letter, replacing the informal words and phrases with more formal ones.

Q3 Make a list of all the adjectives and adverbs in this story, then rewrite the extract with more exciting adjectives and adverbs. Use words from the box below to help you.

> Paul walked slowly down to the dock. The blue boat was still there, docked at the end of the quiet jetty. He hoped very much that the man had gone. There was a storm gathering slowly overhead. He realised quickly that it had grown dark. He took off his shoes and climbed onto the deck. There was the old door, with the scorch marks from the fire still there. From beyond the door he heard a quiet voice:
> "Come in my child. You are welcome here."
> Paul was struck by an awful fear. He knew that voice.

These words are just suggestions. You don't have to use them all.

Adjectives: mysterious   insiduous   eerie   silent   paralysing   familiar   gigantic   perilous   frightening   deafening   gloomy
Adverbs: timidly   self-consciously   rapidly   feverishly   suddenly   distantly   maddeningly   passionately   fearfully

I only know two words...

Hmm. After that joke I'm going to crawl into a small hole and not come out again for eight and a half months, even if someone says "please". Meanwhile, on p37, you've got some spelling practice.

Spelling

There are four marks for spelling on the Shakespeare writing question — that's a fifth of the total marks. Remember to check your spelling when you read through your work at the end.

Q1 There are some words which are easy to mix up when you're in a hurry.
Copy out the sentences below, choosing the right words from the brackets.

a) After the film we went back to [they're / their / there] house for a meal.

b) I wanted to go to the arcade, but when we got [they're / their / there] it was closed.

c) Slowly, I realised that I had no idea [where / wear] I was.

d) Your point of view depends on [whether / weather] or not you live near the worksite.

e) I [brought / bought] some food at the supermarket, before going home.

f) The new show by Pat Gussel is [quite / quiet] entertaining.

g) If you want to win the championship, you will need more [practice / practise].

h) If the manager leaves, the [effect / affect] on the players will be catastrophic.

i) I thought the car had moved, but when I looked again it was [stationary / stationery].

j) Their daughter, [who's / whose] in Manchester, is working in a pub.

Q2 Some words and phrases are really useful for the writing question.
Sketch out the table below, correcting the spelling of the words in the white boxes.

Useful Words and Phrases for the Writing Question		
Starting a formal letter:	Ending a formal letter:	Beginning a speech:
Deer Sir / Madame Deer Mrs Jones	Yours sincerly Yours faithfuly	Welcom Good evning
Persuasive phrases:	Impersonal phrases	Phrases to link paragraphs
We all now that What we shud do now Surly we could	It can be argeud Some poeple believe One point of viuw is	On the othre hand A second raison for this is Anuther importnt concern is

Q3 This paragraph's bursting with bad spelling. Make a list of the words spelt incorrectly, then rewrite the paragraph with correct spelling.

Check your new spellings afterwards with a dictionary. There are 22 mistakes.

Occasionally, I like to visit the centre of town. You can see all the goverment builings which are really big and impressif. There are lots of poeple in the streets, walking and luaghing. The atmospere's brilliant. My favourite place is definitly the cathdral witch is nine hondred years old. Inside the cathdrale it's very cold but the stayned glass windows are beuatiful. There's also a coffee shop their which sells delicous cakes. Seperate from the cathdral is a small chapel which is notorius for haveing nuns buryied inside the walls.

Writing for the Reader or Audience

In the exam you'll have to pretend you're writing for a particular reader or audience, e.g. people in school assembly, readers of the school magazine, a local businessman, a friend...

Q1a) These pieces of writing have been written for different types of reader or audience. Match up each piece of writing (A-D) with its intended reader or audience (i-iv).

> **A** Last week, a local schoolboy got more than he bargained for when he added his mother's rhubarb crumble to a tank of algae. The result of this bizarre experiment? A teacher described it in one word: "Mayhem." The boy, aged 13, cannot be named for legal reasons.

> **B** Last week, I did a really interesting experiment in my school. I tried adding rhubarb crumble to a tank of algae. Do you know what algae is? It's a sort of moss that grows on the surface of ponds. After three days, I found that the algae was growing bigger and bigger.

> **C** Did I tell you that I did an amazing experiment in school last week? We were adding different things to tanks of algae to see what would happen. I added my mum's rhubarb crumble. Blimey, that was a mistake! The algae grew absolutely enormous; it was bigger than Gavin's bike.

> **D** My teacher suggested that I should describe my algae experiment to you, in the hope that you could shed some light on the results. The algae was from a local pond in Haverthwaite. About 50 cm³ was used in a 5 litre tank of water. One standard portion of crumble was added.

(i) A friend   (ii) Readers of a local newspaper   (iii) An expert   (iv) Pupils of a local primary school

b) Write a sentence explaining why each of the texts suits the reader or audience you chose in a). Think about the words, tone and style used.

Q2 Rewrite this newspaper article as if you are telling the same information to a friend in a letter. Make sure you lay it out like a real letter, and start and sign off properly.

Hamster Eats Puma Alive

A local zoo was thrown into chaos yesterday, when a pet rodent entered the puma enclosure and attacked a male puma.

The hamster was brought to the zoo by her owner, 9-year-old Lizzie Thomas. The girl's parents were unaware that she was carrying the rodent in her coat pocket at 3 pm yesterday, when it escaped.

It ran into the enclosure and collected large quantities of the puma's fur in its pouches, before being pulled off by a keeper.

The puma survived, but suffered hair loss

Writing for the Reader or Audience

There'll be information in the writing question which tells you who the reader or audience is. Have a gander at the <u>sample exam question</u> below, then do the questions that follow it.

This is an extract from a school newsletter:

The Karl Smith Young Travel Writer Award

In memory of Karl Smith, the school's gardener from 1978 to 2003, the school is introducing an annual award for the best piece of travel writing by a pupil. This year's entries should include:

- a description of a favourite holiday destination, in Britain or abroad,
- details of the language, architecture/scenery, food and climate.

Entries will be judged by the headteacher.
The local Herald newspaper has agreed to print the winning entry.

Write an entry for the award. You should make your report believable, but your account can be imaginary or based on real experiences.

30 marks

Q1 Who is going to read your entry to the award? Choose from options i)-iv).

i) Karl Smith, the school gardener

ii) The headteacher and the English teachers

iii) The headteacher and possibly readers of the local paper

iv) Iain Duncan-Smith

NB: You don't have to answer the actual exam question.

Q2 Write down all the words from the box which you think describe the tone your entry should have. Write a sentence to explain each choice.

> jokey   persuasive   sarcastic   angry   atmospheric
> indignant   offensive   negative   fairly formal   evocative
> bored   very informal   imaginative   peculiar   positive

Q3 Here's a paragraph from an entry to the "Karl Smith Travel Writer Award". Rewrite the paragraph. Make the tone match the words you chose in Q2.

Hint: start by chopping out bits that seem unsuitable

> The food in Brittany is just brilliant. I bet you don't believe me but I've never tasted anything better and neither has my mum. First off, you don't have to eat rubbish, clichéd French food like croissants and baguettes. Boring!!! There are markets which sell fresh fruit and honey pies; you can eat them for breakfast instead. Though actually my sister got ill on the third day and wasn't able to eat anything at all. Bernadette and Hervé, the French couple we stayed with, were dead nice and they went to the market every day. It was really sunny and you could just wander around buying food and getting a tan.

001110000101000 — writing for robots...

01000001011110100101010000111BILLGATES01000001010011101000000111011101010101110101001111
00100ATEMYMOTHERBOARD101001010011000110011001101010010010011001100100101010111101101001100011

Different Types of Writing

Exam questions always ask you to do a particular <u>type of writing</u>, e.g. a story, letter, speech...
You've got to know tricks for all the different types in order to sweep the examiners off their feet.

Q1   Copy out the table and use words and phrases from the box below to fill in the blanks.

Type of Writing	Typical format/structure	Typical style/tone
Formal letter		Fairly formal and impersonal Written to specific reader(s)
	Begins with a welcoming introduction, followed by paragraphs and conclusion.	Written as if speaking directly to audience
Article/report	Has a headline, sometimes written in columns	
Story	Standard format, in paragraphs, with a beginning, middle and end	
Leaflet		Informative or persuasive Usually fairly formal
	Begins with "Dear..." Ends with informal sign-off, e.g. "Best wishes"	Personal, informal Written to specific reader(s)

Begins with address, and "Dear"
Ends with "Yours sincerely" or "Yours faithfully"

Informal letter

Headings breaking up text, pictures with captions

Speech   Entertaining/imaginative

Informative and impersonal

Q2   *Read through this information, then answer the questions below.*

Mr Tim Hazelwood is a refuse collector. He has been on strike for six weeks for better pay. The binmen in Thorncastle earn £6 per hour, and want this increased to £8 an hour. They think that because it's unpleasant work with unsociable working hours they deserve more pay. The council say they only have a limited budget and many other groups of workers are equally deserving of a pay rise. Mr Tim Hazelwood marched through the centre of Thorncastle on Saturday, wearing only a dustbin, to get publicity for the binmen's cause. He was arrested for indecent exposure.

a)   Use the information in the box to write a short article for the local newspaper about Tim. Write in paragraphs and include a headline, but don't bother setting it out in columns.

To save time, in the test they only get you to do a bit of the layout.

b)   Write a formal letter from the Refuse Collector's Strike Association to Thorncastle's MP explaining why you want more pay. Start your letter "Dear Sandy Johns MP".

c)   Write a short leaflet, to be sent out by the council, telling local residents about the strike. Explain that they'll have to take their own rubbish to the skip during the strike. Lay out your leaflet in paragraphs, and with headings, but don't do any illustrations.

Formal and Informal Writing

For any bit of writing in the SAT, work out whether the tone should be formal or informal, e.g. a tabloid article would be pretty slangy, whereas broadsheets are very formal.

Q1   Read the following sample exam question. Should the answer to the question be very formal, fairly formal or informal? Explain your answer.

New Science Block Brings Joy to School

Your local MP is visiting your school to open a new building. This is a memo from your headteacher:

> We would like a select pupil to give a short speech at the opening of the new science block. The speech should include:
> • A welcome and thank you to the MP for attending the event
> • A light-hearted description of the problems with the old science block
> • A conclusion describing how happy the pupils are that there is now a new science block

Write a speech to be given at the opening of the new building.   *30 marks*

Q2   Rewrite the following paragraphs, making them sound more formal. Keep the same meanings.

a)   Hi everyone, I'm here to tell you about all the stuff that's been happening during the last few weeks at the school. I'll then be showing you around, giving you a chance to chat to some of the kids and letting you have a few drinks and biscuits.

b)   Switzerland is fantastic! There's so much you can do — snowboarding, skiing, walking and shopping. There's even bears you can feed in Basle, though it's pretty cruel that they're kept in captivity, when you think about it.

c)   This paper can reveal exclusively that the main lottery draw has been fixed *three times* in the last year! Our suspicions were aroused when we discovered that supporters of the governing party had been winning significant sums on the lottery. We didn't want to believe it.

Q3   Rewrite the following letter, making it informal in format and tone.

Does my bum look big in this?

> The Old Coach House
> Bowden
> RH3 7RL
>
> The Grange
> Oxton
> LH4 8PW
>
> Dear Josephine Baker,
>
> I am writing to ask your advice on a rather personal matter. Since I was young, I have enjoyed gymnastics, and had hoped to continue taking part in this sport for the rest of my life.
> Recently, however, I have started to suffer from rheumatism, which I believe is common among people of my advanced years.
> I have heard that, before you retired, you spent some years as a homeopathist. Do you have any recommendations for herbal remedies which might ease my pain, and enable me to backflip again? Any advice would be gratefully received.
>
> Yours sincerely,
> Bessie Smith

Writing to Inform, Explain and Describe

The examiners split all the different styles of writing up into <u>four</u> "writing purposes".
The first is to '<u>inform, explain or describe</u>' — basically, telling the reader some information.

Q1   Which of these types of writing are of the 'inform, explain, describe' type?
       Choose one or more from options i)-v) and explain your choices.

   i)   Instructions for a new pupil on what to do on their first day of school.

   ii)   A political leaflet telling people to vote Liberal Democrat.

   iii)   An account of what a place is like — its scenery, climate and architecture.

   iv)   A newspaper article commenting on the two sides of an argument between
       the council and a burger restaurant.

   v)   An article about a person you admire and the contribution they have made to
       your local area.

Q2a)   Below are three possible introductions to an 'inform, explain, describe' article (1-3).
       Match them up to the readers they have been written for (A-C).

  1) | Orson Welles was a really important director. He made a famous film, called 'Citizen Kane',
a long time ago. It had a massive impact on how films were made, and how people told
stories on film. This article is going to explain what was so special about 'Citizen Kane'.

  2) | Orson Welles is one of the most written about and controversial directors in film history. As
you know, his most famous film 'Citizen Kane' (1941) has recently been the subject of criticism.
In this article, I want to return the focus to what made 'Citizen Kane' a great film, and the
many ways it changed the course of film history.

  3) | Orson Welles is one of the most exciting directors in film history. You have probably heard of his
most famous film, 'Citizen Kane', made in 1941. What you might not realise is the huge impact it
had on how films were made and how stories were told on film. That's what this article is all about.

  A)   Adult readers of the local paper who have probably heard of 'Citizen Kane'.

  B)   Younger pupils at your school who probably know nothing about 'Citizen Kane'.

  C)   The readers of a local film newsletter, who know quite a lot about 'Citizen Kane'.

  b)   For each introduction, explain how you can tell which audience it's written for.

Who's this?
See p58.

Q3   Write two paragraphs about your favourite film. Describe the plot and explain
       why you think it's good. Pretend the reader hasn't heard of the film before.

My favourite film is Kodak...

Informing, explaining and describing are pretty similar. Informing is telling someone useful information, explaining
is telling someone what information means and describing is telling someone all the details... you can often do all three at once.

Writing to Inform, Explain and Describe

Be <u>clear</u> when you're writing to 'inform, explain or describe'. Write about things in a logical order and explain tricky words. Use interesting vocab too — don't let it get dull...

Q1 Rewrite these paragraphs. For each one, put the sentences into a logical order.

a) It has an unusually hot climate. Past the olive groves, there is a river which is known locally as the 'Devil's River'. In Normandy, there is a very beautiful valley called the Gorge Rancré. The name originated in an ancient local myth that an animal had to be drowned in the river each year to keep the devil happy. This means that olive groves and vines can flourish there.

b) Anne was executed as a result. Therefore, charges of adultery were brought against Anne. This was important to Henry because he wanted a male heir to the throne. These charges were probably untrue, but it didn't matter because Henry was so powerful. Henry VIII decided he wanted to get rid of Anne Boleyn because she had failed to bear him a son.

Q2 Copy out these sentences taken from an 'inform, explain, describe' answer, changing the highlighted words to words from the cloud. Choose vocab that makes the sentences clearer.

a) The doctor will give you some stuff to do at home, so you can strengthen the muscle.
b) Do you like nice food? Then this is the article for you.
c) The new headmaster is very quiet and a bit scary. He knows too much about me.
d) Telescopes are great because they let you see things far away.

proper   facts   poverty   delicious   incredibly   nonsensical   poor quality   distant objects   exercises   sarcastic

Q3 The following sentences contain words which you might think are easy, but other people could find tricky. Rewrite each sentence, adding a short definition or explanation of the tricky word.

e.g. The ingredients for the recipe include fennel.
The ingredients for the recipe include fennel, which is a green, leafy vegetable.

a) The computer has a spell-checker.
b) My grandfather was an air-raid warden.
c) Liverpool is a multicultural city.
d) The striker was clearly offside.

It's important to make your writing as clear as possible. If you use tricky or technical words, make sure you include a definition.

Q4 The following descriptive paragraph is really dull. Rewrite it making it more interesting, but keeping the same meaning. Try adding adjectives and adverbs and changing the verbs.

I went to the local funfair at the weekend. The rides were good. I went on the waltzer, but it made me feel ill. Then I went on the roller-coaster, and it was great. I liked going upside down, and seeing all the people on the ground. When I got off the roller-coaster I saw a friend from school but he went away before I could speak to him. Before I left I ate some candyfloss, which was really good.

Some of the really dull bits have been highlighted to get you started.

Writing to Persuade, Argue and Advise

The second type of writing exam question is 'persuade, argue and advise'. It's all about persuading someone to either agree with your point of view, or to take your advice on an issue.

Q1 Which of the following are tricks you can use to make your writing more persuasive? Choose one or more from options i)-v) and write them down.

i) Keep your writing polite. Don't intentionally offend people who disagree with your views.

ii) Use humour, contrast and repetition to put people off your main point.

iii) Use descriptive words to emphasise your points.

iv) Ally yourself with the reader by saying "us" and "we" and using rhetorical questions.

v) Back up your points with elephants.

Rhetorical questions are ones which don't expect an answer, e.g. "Surely we all know that Darwin was right?"

Q2 Rewrite the following sentences, changing the language to make them sound less vague and more convincing.

a) People should maybe think about the effect smoking could have on their health before they try cigarettes.

b) One question we might ask is, "If the government have evidence about why we should eat spinach, would they mind sharing it with us?"

c) If you don't want to go on the trip, it's probably best if you ask your mother to write a letter to the teacher explaining why.

Q3 Using adjectives makes your writing more persuasive, and adjectives work really well in groups of three. Copy down the sentences and fill in the blanks with adjectives.

e.g. **We need to keep the local park; it is <u>peaceful</u>, <u>beautiful</u> and <u>unique</u>.**

There's more than one possible answer for each of these.

a) I enjoy swimming because it is relaxing, fun and ....

b) It's important to read the newspapers because they are thought-provoking, ... and ....

c) We all know that homework is .... , ... and ....

Q4 If you are writing to offer someone advice, you should suggest things — not insist on them. Change the following commands into suggestions.

e.g. You must do what the teacher says.
It would be a good idea to do what the teacher says.

a) You have to take part in the race.

b) Leave your job.

c) Come swimming at the leisure centre tomorrow.

d) Make your mind up.

I suggest that you leave the pool now.

Writing to Persuade, Argue and Advise

You can't ignore other people's points of view. To argue that your opinion is right, you need to say why other opinions are wrong. "You're wrong cos you smell of poo" doesn't cut the mustard.

Q1 Are the following paragraphs persuasive, or not?
Explain each of your answers.

a) You should vote for Claire Harris if you want to see an improvement in employment and a clamping down on crime in the local area. These are areas in which she is very strong; her Young Offenders Scheme is ample evidence of this. On the other hand, you could vote for Edward Jones. He has agreed to increase spending on health and education, which are important issues for many people.

b) You should vote for Claire Harris because she is intelligent, honest and cares about the local area. Her scheme to help young offenders back into employment has been a major success and the envy of other constituencies. People backing Edward Jones forget the appalling crime and unemployment rates which this constituency suffered the last time he was in power.

Q2 Use the evidence from the boxes below to make two properly backed-up paragraphs, following on from the opening lines a) and b).

a) The death penalty should not be reintroduced in Britain.

b) The death penalty should be reintroduced in Britain.

Keeping people in prison costs the government money — for buildings, staff, food and healthcare. People who have committed horrific crimes and are sentenced to life imprisonment are wasting government resources.	There have been several recent cases in Britain where long-serving prisoners have been found innocent because of new evidence. If we had the death penalty in Britain these people would have been wrongly executed long ago.
Lord Justice Hodgeman has said on this issue, "Although I have great faith in the British legal system, we should not lie to ourselves that it is infallible."	Reintroducing the death penalty would also act as a deterrent to criminals. It would show them that the legal system in Britain is strong and won't let them get away lightly with their crimes.

Q3 Write a short article for your school newsletter arguing **either** that cars should be allowed in the school playground **or** that cars should be banned from the school playground. Mention all of the points from the table below in your article.

Why Cars Should be Allowed in the Playground	Why Cars Shouldn't be Allowed in the Playground
It is hard for teachers to find other parking nearby.	They increase the amount of noise outside school.
It is the safest place for teachers to leave their cars.	Children might be run over and injured or killed.
As long as people drive slowly, it should be safe.	It means there is less space for children to play and exercise.

Writing to Imagine, Explore and Entertain

This is the third type of writing question. <u>Imaginative</u> and <u>entertaining</u> writing means getting the reader involved in a text using pace, suspense, humour and interesting language. Writing to <u>explore</u> means thoughtful writing about your personal experiences and reactions to events, e.g. in a diary.

Q1　A good story follows a good structure. Put these parts of a story in the right order.

　i)　a satisfying ending, which resolves the crisis

　ii)　a crisis

　iii)　a gripping opening to the story

　iv)　development of the plot, characters and setting established in the opening

crisis = a period of trouble or danger

Q2　Comparisons make descriptions of characters and settings more interesting. Copy and complete the sentences below, adding a word to each to complete the comparison.

e.g.　Paul was so scared that he wobbled like a ....
　　Paul was so scared that he wobbled like a _jelly_.

The posh word for this sort of comparison is 'simile'

　a)　Ilona turned to the headteacher furiously and screamed like a ....

　b)　As he crept over to the side of the ship, Bob's shoes squeaked like ....

　c)　The atmosphere in the dentist's waiting room was like a ....

There's more than one possible answer for each of these.

　d)　The chips looked gorgeous. Henry was as hungry as a ....

Q3　Write a description of each thing below, using alliteration to make it more effective.

　e.g. snake　➡　***The snake slithered subtly across the sparkling sand.***

　　a) storm　　　　b) cat

i.e. start off a few words with the same letter

Q4　Write a list of onomatopoeic words that you could use to describe each thing.

　e.g. piano music　➡　***crash, plink-plonk, trill, murmur...***

　　a) explosion　　　b) Grand Prix start

onomatopoeia = words that sound like the noise they describe

Q5　Rewrite this paragraph, replacing the highlighted clichés with more interesting language.

　　Then, the icing on the cake — who should walk in but my old nemesis, Miss Rumple! That was a shock to the system. I had no room for manoeuvre; I had to take the bull by the horns. So I took the catapult from my pocket, saying to myself, "It's not over until the fat lady sings."

Q6　Match up each of the characters below to four words from the box that you might use to describe them.

If you don't know a word, look it up.

　(a) **Henry, a shy boy who likes running.**　　(b) **Mrs Henderson, a bossy shop keeper.**　　(c) **Pau, a pop sensation from Catalonia.**

| authoritarian | athletic | intimidating | fashionable | famous | timid |
| glamorous | musical | ancient | introverted | garrulous | fit |

Writing — Writing for Different Purposes

Writing to Imagine, Explore and Entertain

Keep the tone and style the same all the way through a piece of imaginative writing. If you're writing from someone else's point of view, don't slip up and start writing as yourself.

Q1   Which of the following paragraphs has more suspense? Explain your answer.

   i)   There was a cat in the bag. Josephine didn't know what was in there and wanted to find out, so she put her hand in the bag. She screamed when she felt the cat's fur.

   ii) Josephine approached the bag cautiously. She had to find out what was in there. As she reached in, her fingers felt something furry. She screamed. It was a cat!

Q2   Rewrite these paragraphs, making the pace seem faster, but keeping the same meaning. Try splitting them up into smaller sentences and including direct speech.

   a)   She was sitting quietly on a bench in the park and didn't seem scared. I rushed up and told her that she should run away as fast as possible, but she didn't seem to understand.

   b)   The warrior Xenodwarf wielded his sword and told his enemy to prepare for death. To his surprise the enemy refused to surrender and did a nifty flying kick towards his right ear.

Q3   You can sometimes be asked to write from someone else's point of view — imagining that you are that person. The following paragraph has been written using third person narration. Rewrite it as if you are Sarah telling the story (from the point of view of 'I').

> Sarah was led through the servants' quarters towards the big kitchens. She felt scared, and trembled visibly. The only time she had been to the manor before was to deliver a message for her sister who worked there as a lady's maid. Even then she had been frightened. There were stories about the manor; people in the village said there were so many corridors under the house it was like a maze. A boy had been lost down there, in a game of hide and seek. The rumour was that he was still alive.

Q4   Read the newspaper article below, and write a letter by Sterling Hayden to his daughter describing the events.

Sea Captain Reveals His Salsa Hell

A lone yachtsman was unable to land on shore for three months, because of his newly-developed addiction to salsa dancing. Wizened former sea captain Sterling Hayden told this newspaper that he had first started dancing when he watched a salsa-based exercise video his daughter lent him to help him keep in shape.

Says Sterling, "At first it was fun; I enjoyed tapping my toes. But soon I was in the throes of addiction. I couldn't steer or keep course because the urge to dance was so strong. After three months, I finally recovered after finding a Bach CD under a life jacket."

Q5   Imagine you have an older sister or brother who's recently got married. Write a short diary entry exploring your thoughts about the marriage. Use the points below to help you.

• What is your sibling's new husband/wife like? Do you get on with them?
• How did the news they were getting married make you feel? (e.g. jealous, excited)
• What was the ceremony like? Did you play any part in it? (e.g. bridesmaid)

Writing to Analyse, Review and Comment

The last type of writing you could get in the exam is 'analyse, review and comment'. This means discussing a subject without ranting about your opinions — you have to sound detached.

Q1   Make writing sound impersonal when you're writing an analysis. Rewrite these sentences, changing the language to be more detached and neutral.

e.g.   I don't like the programmes on children's television; they're really patronising.

Some teenagers don't enjoy the programmes on children's television; they think that the programmes are patronising.

a)   I think children over 14 should be allowed to go on holiday by themselves; I know that I enjoy very different holiday activities to my parents.

b)   I think it's disgusting that confectionery and fast-food manufacturers can advertise on television, persuading children to eat food that is really unhealthy.

c)   Surely everyone knows that the government is trying to introduce stealth taxes on mobile phones?

Q2   Sweeping statements make you sound <u>biased</u>. Rewrite these sentences to make them sound more cautious. Use words and phrases from the box to help you.

a)   The greenhouse effect is having a terrible effect on the Earth's environment.

b)   If the Green Party got into power, it would be great for Britain and great for the environment.

c)   Dogs make very good pets because they force people to go for walks and get some fresh air.

d)   Trains are never on time.

Don't use any of the phrases more than once.

It is possible that...   Some people believe...   might   could   perhaps
One point of view is that...   maybe   often   sometimes   can

Q3   Use the following plan to write a short newspaper article commenting on the building of a new football stadium in the centre of town.

Should there be a new football stadium in the centre of Sudley?	
Group of people:	Their opinions about the new stadium:
Managers of the football club	It will be bigger than the old one, so more fans can watch the match. More profit can be made.
Some local residents	Worries about the noise, traffic congestion and football hooligans in the centre of town.
Local shopkeepers and businesses	Might bring more people into the town centre. Pubs and food outlets might profit.

Writing to Analyse, Review and Comment

Analytical writing is very different to persuasive writing. Your aim here is to show the examiner you've considered different opinions and evidence as objectively as possible.

Q1   You need to look at both sides of the argument when you're writing to 'analyse, comment and review'. Copy the table below. Write in three reasons to support each opinion.

Should the Royal Family have their privileged position taken away and become a normal family?	
Opinion: **YES**	Opinion: **NO**
Reason 1:	Reason 1:
Reason 2:	Reason 2:
Reason 3:	Reason 3:

Q2   Conclusions to essays can be tricky — you have to give your opinion, but still sound reasonable and objective. Explain why each of these conclusions is good or bad.

Being objective means writing about both sides of an argument.

a)   In conclusion, some people are very worried by the rapid destruction of the rainforests. The rainforests are very hard to replace and wildlife are losing their habitats. On the other hand the people who live there need farmland to make a living. It's a really difficult issue and hard to reach a conclusion about.

b)   As shown in the above essay, there are strong arguments on both sides. I personally believe that alternatives need to be found to the deforestation of the rainforests because of the long-term bad effects on the environment. People may gain farmland from clearing rainforests, but the land soon becomes infertile. Other solutions need to be found to create livelihoods for people in the region, so that the rainforests and environment can be protected.

I wholeheartedly agree.

c)   I am going to conclude this essay with my personal opinion about the topic. I strongly believe that the rainforests shouldn't be cut down. Any other views are deeply misguided. It shows a real lack of intelligence that people could destroy something so precious. We should all campaign to stop the destruction of the rainforests.

Just write the conclusion, not the whole essay.

Q3   Look back at the table you wrote for Q1. Write a conclusion for the essay.

Don't believe a word Anna says — analyse...

It's a confusing world we're living in. By the end of this section you'll have it sussed. Well, you'll know the difference between persuading, analysing, imagining and informing anyway.

Paragraphs

Whatever kind of writing you're asked to do in the exam, you <u>have</u> to write in paragraphs. It gives your writing structure and gets you marks.

Q1   1-5 below are the reasons for starting a new paragraph.
Match them with the paragraph changes in the bits of writing labelled a)-e).

① new point / topic   **②** new person   **③** different person speaks
④ new time being described   **⑤** new place being described

a The Red Scare of 1919 was a time of paranoia in America about left-wing radicals. The Sacco and Vanzetti trial is a famous example.
The McCarthy communist witchhunts were a similar phenomenon. Prominent figures, for example in the film industry, were accused of being communists.

b Algeria was colonised in 1830 and remained under French rule until the revolution of the 1950s. The revolution was very violent and lasted from 1954 to 1962.
Egypt was quite different. It was never fully colonised, but was under a British protectorate from 1881.

c John walked over to the ostrich and raised his hat.
"How do you do sir?" he asked politely. However, the ostrich did not reply.

d Kirsty felt really angry about the play. She kicked the old lady sitting in front of her in frustration.
The old lady turned round and grinned a terrible grin. Slowly, she raised her stick.

e Ernest Hemingway used to live in Key West in Florida. His favourite bar there was called Sloppy Joe's.
If you go to Sloppy Joe's now it's in a different building and is just a tourist trap.

Trapped! Hope I can get out of here by Christmas...

Q2   A good paragraph sticks to one topic. Work out which sentences in the following paragraph are rambling off the main topic. Then write out a corrected version.

Pompeii was a small city of no great importance in the Roman world. Seneca does mention the town of Ostia in two of his letters. One of the few mentions Pompeii gets in ancient texts is in relation to a fight which broke out at the amphitheatre in which several people were killed. We can glean more information from the archaeological excavations at the site. From the size of the site it is estimated that it had about twenty thousand inhabitants. Pliny didn't live there, although he was killed by inhaling ash from the eruption. Evidence from the site includes: buildings, the contents of people's houses, wall paintings, graffiti and plaster casts of people who died in the eruption.

Q3   Copy out this bit from a short story, starting new paragraphs where needed.

As Myrna sat down at the kitchen table she already felt full. So far she had eaten five blueberry tarts, ten Easter eggs, a rhubarb crumble and 76 fun-size chocolate bars. Ali ran into the room and saw the last piece of evidence, the double-cream layered pavlova still there on the kitchen table. "Come on, he's almost here!" he yelled. "I'm trying," groaned Myrna. Meanwhile, the dastardly Mr Smiker was walking slowly across the fields, his nose twitching in the breeze. The unmistakable scent of a missing double-cream layered pavlova filled his monstrous nostrils. He smiled a terrifying smile. Even his teeth were evil.

Paragraphs

Look — more paragraph questions. Fun, fun, fun.

Q1   Here's a paragraph from a persuasive essay. Rearrange the sentences into the following order: 1) main point, 2) development of main point, 3) evidence (quotes and statistics).

Seventy-five students make use of the bus service; that's a lot of extra cars. If our school bus was discontinued each child would have to travel to school individually. As the headteacher has said, "The pollution caused by the extra cars travelling to the school would have a bad effect on the environment." We all know that school buses are environmentally friendly.

Q2   Read the following paragraphs. Write a first sentence for each paragraph which introduces the main point it is making.

a)   From this point of view, a foetus is a human being with the same value as a baby which has already been born. Julia Donovan of the Pro-Life League says that "People have to put aside their concerns for the mother and think about the child; abortion is effectively murdering a baby." Midwife Deborah Ash agrees, claiming that people who support abortion have not considered the realities of the operation.

b)   From this point of view the rights of the mother are more important than those of the foetus. For example, Bethany Maine of the Women's Rights Association argues that "People who argue against abortion often have no understanding of the difficult situations some women face. Women must have control of their own bodies and be able to choose whether or not to bring a baby into the world."

Q3   If you're describing an event you should write things down in the order they happened. Put these sentences in order and write them out as a paragraph.

- Hillary had been annoyed; she'd wanted to have an adventure, not to go home.
- Once, when Hillary was at primary school, she'd climbed over the playing field fence.
- Hillary had refused to be scared and had started walking as far from school as possible.
- After about two hours she had reached her own house.
- All her friends had run away because they were scared.

Q4   You can compare and contrast two things within a paragraph. Which of the following paragraphs does this well, and which does it badly? Explain your answer.

a
Winter is brilliant. If you're lucky it snows and you can go sledging and have snowball fights. The only real problem is that people have more colds and the days are shorter. In summer the weather's hot and you get sunburn, although the days are longer.

b
Winter is brilliant. If you're lucky it snows and you can go sledging and have snowball fights. I like skidding around on the ice too. The build-up to Christmas is great, and it gets dark early, which is fun and spooky. I don't like summer though.

Q5   Write a paragraph comparing cities and the countryside.

Linking Paragraphs

OK, so now your paragraph writing is so polished, you could eat your dinner off it.
You've still got to make sure your paragraphs flow — i.e. follow on nicely from each other.

Q1 Write out the words or phrases below (i-xii) that are useful for linking paragraphs together.

i)	furthermore	vii)	milking it
ii)	another point of view is	viii)	however
iii)	with hindsight	ix)	another example of
iv)	gregarious types	x)	in addition to this
v)	too right	xi)	beyond comprehension
vi)	a contrasting view is	xii)	on the other hand

Q2 A new paragraph should use a linking word or phrase to join it to the paragraph before.
Read these paragraphs and write an opening sentence for the paragraph that follows.

e.g. Cary Grant was a suave actor, at his peak in the 1940s and 1950s. Originally he was from Bristol, and his real name was Archibald Leach.

[The next paragraph is going to be about Ingrid Bergman, a movie star in the 1940s and 1950s.]

Another popular movie star from the 1940s and 1950s was the actress Ingrid Bergman.

a Many years ago white lead was used in face powder. This resulted in women suffering from lead poisoning, although they didn't know what the cause of the illness was.

[The next paragraph is going to be about how nowadays people know white lead is dangerous and don't use it for make-up.]

b The opinion of the school's board of governors about truancy is fairly harsh. They suggest that pupils should be punished with detentions, and that the parents of repeat offenders should be sent warning letters and fines.

[The next paragraph is about the opinion of the Parent's Association, which is less harsh.]

c Many young children enjoy cartoons. They are bright and appealing to look at and feature easily recognisable characters. A lot of imagination and humour is put into popular cartoons, and this attracts children's interest.

[The next paragraph is going to be about how many parents disapprove of cartoons because they think they are mindless drivel.]

Q3 Write two paragraphs. In the first one describe the village, town or city where you lived when you were ten. In the second paragraph describe the primary school you went to there. Link the two paragraphs together smoothly.

Q4 Write two paragraphs: the first describing your views about fashion, the second describing your parents' views about fashion. Link the two paragraphs together smoothly.

Writing — Text Structure and Organisation

Writing Good Introductions

The introduction is the first thing the examiner will read. So make sure it's a good 'un.

Q1 Pretend you are writing a <u>speech</u> to give to the Parent-Teacher Association of your school. Which of the following words and phrases, i)-x), would be good to use in your introduction?

i) Good morrow fair gentlemen

ii) Good evening

iii) Okey-dokey

iv) We are here tonight to discuss

v) We are here tonight to rant about

vi) In my introduction to this essay

vii) Hi, it's darn good you could all come tonight

viii) Welcome

ix) In conclusion

x) The key issue I am going to discuss is

Q2 In a <u>persuasive</u> essay you need to make sure your argument is clear in the introduction. Which of these introductions does this better? Explain why.

Remember — persuasive essays are very different from analysing essays.

i)
> The issue of security is important in modern schools. Tragedies have taken place when violent outsiders have been able to walk unchallenged into school grounds. If security isn't improved in all schools, we have to ask ourselves: how long will it be before another tragedy happens?

ii)
> The issue of security is important in modern schools. A lot of schools have increased security since a series of violent incidents over the last few years. Some people think this is the right course of action to protect children. Others believe it creates an unhealthy atmosphere of fear and paranoia.

Q3 Below is part of an essay plan. It's for an essay <u>analysing</u> the effect of advertising on children's television. Use the plan to write a full introduction to the essay.

> <u>Good points</u>
> 1. money from advertising helps to fund non-BBC programming, including good children's programmes.
> 2. adverts are often entertaining, with imagination and humour that children enjoy.
> <u>Language to use:</u> remember to be impersonal/objective/cautious when analysing
>
> <u>Bad points</u>
> 1. advertising persuades children to buy sweets and junk food which is unhealthy for them.
> 2. advertising encourages children to want expensive toys, which their parents might not be able to afford.

Q4 The notepad below shows an author's notes for the introduction of an <u>imaginative story</u>, called 'Ladykiller Bob'. Use the information on the notepad to write an introduction to the story.

What happens	How it should feel
• Bob is getting ready for a night out	Happy, lighthearted
• He turns on some funky tunes	
• He opens his wardrobe — all his clothes have been torn to shreds	dramatic/surprising
• Bob hears a noise downstairs	scary — what's going to happen next?

Don't write more than six sentences for your introduction.

Structuring the Middle Bit

The basic structure for all your writing should be: introduction, middle paragraphs and conclusion. To really impress the examiner you'll need to structure your middle paragraphs too.

Q1 The boxes i)-vi) below summarise the types of paragraphs in a typical <u>persuasive</u> essay. Put i)-vi) into a logical order and write them out.

i) Give a reason to support your argument. Back it up with evidence.

ii) Conclusion — bring together main points why your argument's right.

iii) Give a reason why people might not agree with your argument. Give evidence of why they are wrong.

iv) Give a second reason why people might not agree with your argument. Give evidence of why they are wrong.

v) Introduction — outline your main argument.

vi) Give a second reason to support your argument. Back it up with evidence.

Q2 These plans are for an essay <u>analysing</u> whether it's good to live in the countryside. One of them's not as well structured as the others. Decide which it is and say why.

i) **Introduction**
<u>Advantages</u>
1. wildlife, great scenery
2. fresh air
3. good outdoor activities
4. less noise pollution
<u>Disadvantages</u>
1. public transport feeble
2. less access to good libraries/museums/cultural events than in a town
3. fewer jobs available
Conclusion

ii) **Introduction**
<u>Advantage 1</u> the countryside is a great place to live because of the wildlife, scenery and fresh air.
<u>Advantage 2</u> There are some really interesting jobs e.g. in conservation.
<u>Advantage 3</u> There are lots of brilliant outdoor activities, e.g. canoeing and rock climbing.
Conclusion

iii) **Introduction**
1. <u>adv</u>: good outdoor activities
   <u>disadv</u>: fewer cultural activities, e.g. theatres
2. <u>adv</u>: fresh air and less noise pollution
   <u>disadv</u>: less public transport; often have to rely on car
3. <u>adv</u>: wildlife and scenery
   <u>disadv</u>: fewer jobs than in towns
Conclusion

Q3 Write down the correct chronological order for these paragraphs.

chronological — in the order of when things happened

i) We now know that the body Schliemann found in Grave Circle A is unlikely to be that of Agamemnon. The graves date from c.1500 BC, while the Trojan War probably happened in 1200-1100 BC.

ii) The ruined cities of Tiryns, Mycenae and Pylos in Greece date from as far back as 1500 BC. They are mentioned in Homer's epic poems 'The Iliad' and 'The Odyssey'. For example, the character Agamemnon in 'The Iliad' is called the ruler of Mycenae.

iii) The ruins of Mycenae were excavated by the German archaeologist Heinrich Schliemann in the nineteenth century. He was a romantic man. When he found a golden death mask in Grave Circle A at Mycenae, he claimed that he had "seen the face of Agamemnon".

iv) Further excavations are still happening at Mycenae. Archaeologists want to find out more about ancient Mycenean religions; evidence so far includes frescoes, shrines and statues of goddesses. How much more can they find in the ruins of this great city?

Structuring the Middle Bit

The exam questions give you lots of hints you can use to structure your essay — and for the long writing question you get a planning grid so you can do a good, structured plan.

Q1   *Read the following short writing question and then do parts a) and b).*

Last Night Out Before Revision

Your school is organising a meal out for Year 9 pupils before revision begins for the SATs.

> For the attention of Year 9 pupils:
> The school has decided to pay for a free meal out on the eve of the revision period.
> The headteacher urges pupils to remember that:
> • the SATs will be over soon
> • all their hard work will be rewarded with good grades
> • pupils who don't work hard will regret it later

Write a speech that the headteacher will give at the meal.   *20 marks including 4 marks for spelling*

---

a)   Write down three key topics you would need to cover in your answer to the question.

b)   Write down your three key topics on a piece of paper as headings.
Then write down two points you could make under each heading.

Q2   *Read the following long writing question and accompanying planning page.*

Kill Your Speed

This is an extract from a newspaper article:

> Speed limits must be reduced in urban areas. The current risk to lives from traffic is too great. If a driver runs over a pedestrian when he is doing 20 mph, there is a one in five chance he will kill them. This is already a high risk — so why are city speed limits usually as high as 30 mph? Being in a hurry is no excuse. Neither are the improvements in traffic control and pedestrian crossings.

Write a letter to the newspaper in reply, arguing either for or against a reduction in city speed limits.

30 marks

Use this page to plan your work.

arguments supporting your point of view	opinions which disagree with your point of view

---

a)   Copy the planning page out onto an A4 sheet. Fill in two points under each of the main headings using information and ideas mentioned in the question itself.

b)   Write down two more points, of your own, under each of the main headings.

c)   Number the points you have under each heading in order of importance. Cross out any which seem unimportant.

> *By the end of c) you'll have a good essay plan — just the kind of thing you'll want in the exam.*

Middle bit — Keeps your nose away from your feet...

Always put the most important points first — that way you'll have time to explain them properly and if you end up leaving anything out, it'll be the minor points. Helpful advice continues overleaf...

Writing — Text Structure and Organisation

Pointing Out the Structure for the Reader

Structuring your essay is worth marks — so make sure your sleepy examiner realises what you're doing. Big signposts going "Hey buster, my conclusion's over here," ought to do the trick.

Q1 Which of the following introductions (i-iii) signpost clearly what the structure of the leaflet is going to be? Explain how.

> **i** Schools can help the environment; a few simple things can make a big difference. We all know that recycling is important, but so are many other issues, for example educating children about the environment. This leaflet is all about how you can make your school environmentally friendly.

> **ii** Schools can help the environment; a few simple things can make a big difference. This leaflet provides information about easy steps schools can take. Three main areas are covered: recycling and reusing materials, school bus services and educating pupils about the environment.

> **iii** Schools can help the environment, for example by recycling and reusing materials in class. This is very easy to do — try turning a painting over and doing another on the back. Simple! This leaflet will give you loads of other hints for making your school a greener place.

Q2 Signposting the structure of an essay is good, because it lets the reader know what to expect. Write out the phrases and sentences below that would be useful for this.

i) The main argument in favour of this will be dealt with first.

ii) The second half of this essay will discuss the disadvantages...

iii) Without a doubt, nothing can be done about this situation.

iv) There are three main issues at stake here; they will be discussed in turn.

v) The first half of this essay will discuss the advantages...

vi) The second reason for supporting this point of view...

vii) Finally, this essay will consider the impact on...

viii) This is a controversial topic.

Learn and use the good phrases — they'll really impress the examiners.

Q3 Below is part of an analytical essay discussing the advantages and disadvantages of building a new sports hall. Copy out the paragraphs, inserting phrases like those you chose in Q2 to signpost the structure of the essay.

> The new sports hall is a major facility that the school currently lacks. At the moment children have to travel to the local leisure centre to do P.E. and this is a waste of valuable lesson time.
>
> Exercise is a really important part of education. It helps make people healthy and happy. It would be good if the school could offer a wider range of sporting activities and a new sports hall would enable this.
>
> The proposed site for the new sports hall is far from ideal. The plan is to build it on the site of the old and beautiful school garden. Many people disagree with this strongly.
>
> This is the only place, other than the playground, where children can sit and relax at breaktimes. The importance of a peaceful place in a busy school cannot be dismissed lightly.

Writing Good Conclusions

Phew... on to the conclusion already. The conclusion is the <u>last paragraph</u> of your essay. It should bring everything together and tie it up nicely — in a triple reef knot perhaps.

Q1 Is the following statement true or false? Explain your answer.

"The conclusion is a good place to bring in new information. There is no need to be consistent with what has gone before in the essay — capturing the reader's interest is key."

Q2 Which three of the following things (i-viii) should you include in a conclusion?

i) a final statement about the topic

ii) a small Mercedes to bribe the examiner

iii) a summary of the main points in your essay

iv) all the points in your essay explained in detail

v) an introduction to a new topic

vi) a rant about what you think

vii) yesterday's mashed potatoes

viii) your own view on the topic

Q3 The main points made in a persuasive essay are shown by the bullet points below. Write a conclusion for the essay based on these bullet points.

<u>*Should testing on animals be allowed?*</u>

<u>Main points made in essay</u>:

- *I believe that any unnecessary testing on animals should be banned.*

- *Testing on animals is very cruel. Research shows that animals feel pain just like humans.*

- *Animals are often bred purely to be tested on. They are not given the chance to experience any freedom in their life at all.*

- *Make-up is still sometimes tested on animals, which seems unnecessary as this could be tested on humans instead.*

- *Some people argue that testing on animals is necessary in order to develop new medicines to cure diseases that cause many people to suffer. However, I believe that testing on animals should be kept to a minimum to stop animals suffering.*

Q4 An imaginative story needs a logical, satisfactory ending. Here's a summary of the middle section of the story 'Ladykiller Bob' (see page 53). Write an ending paragraph for the story.

What happens next

- There is a fire safety axe behind the door. Bob smashes the glass and takes the axe.
- He ventures downstairs — his dog is lying dead at the bottom of the stairs. Bob puts down the axe and howls with grief. Only his daughter Velma could have done this.
- Through the door Velma emerges. She laughs at Bob, and says "You always were a sap, forget about the dog, I want your money. Where's the safe?"
- Bob thinks quickly. "Velma" he says, "You're my only daughter, you can have all the money you want. It's in the cellar — in the room you played in as a child."

Hint: keep gore to a minimum, or I'll be in trouble with your teacher.

The end of the essay is nigh...

Don't go thinking "and they all lived happily ever after..." is going to do it, coz that won't even bring a twitch of a smile to those stoney-faced examiners. Write a conclusion and write it good.

The Long Writing Question

The long writing question is worth 30 marks. You need to think carefully about what you're going to write — and remember all the things you've practised in this section. Here's an example of a long writing question. The next three pages lead you through how to answer it well.

Should pupils do homework?

This is an extract from the 'Learning in Britain' website, written by teacher Edna Monich:

> We need to open up a discussion about how much homework pupils are given. Some of my Year 9 students have up to two hours of homework each evening. This makes them feel stressed and tired, and stops them from taking part in extra-curricular activities. Homework may allow children to practise skills and learn information, but that is no excuse to give them excessive amounts of work.

Write an article for your school magazine about homework. Argue <u>either</u> that homework is useful, <u>or</u> that pupils should be given less homework.

30 marks

Q1 a) Who is <u>your</u> article supposed to be aimed at? Choose from options i)-iv).

   i) teachers in the North West

      ii) a mixture of teachers, pupils and parents

   iii) the readers of the 'Learning in Britain' website

      iv) Edna Monich

b) Write down the part of the question which lets you know who will read your article.

Q2 a) Write out the words below which you think describe the tone appropriate for the article.

   friendly   informal   angry   happy-go-lucky
   humorous
   formal   polite   offensive   sarcastic

b) Explain why you picked those words.

The Cheese-headed Man

Was he born like that?

Does he know what he looks like?

Or is he merely carrying the cheese?

Nobody knows.

Q3 a) What is the purpose of the article? Choose from options i)-iv).

   i)   to inform, explain or describe
   ii)   to persuade, argue or advise
   iii) to imagine, explore or entertain
   iv)   to analyse, review or comment

b) Write a sentence explaining what this purpose means in your own words.

The Long Writing Question

There's a planning page on the exam paper to help you plan your answer to the long writing question. You're given 15 minutes to plan your answer. The planning page below goes with the SAT question on page 58. Copy it out onto a piece of A4 paper and then answer the questions below.

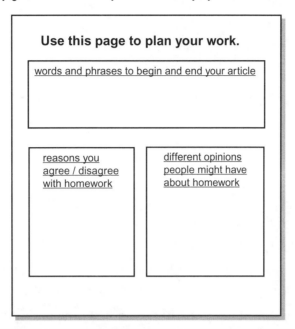

Use this page to plan your work.

words and phrases to begin and end your article

reasons you agree / disagree with homework

different opinions people might have about homework

Q1a) Which of the following sets of words and phrases do you think would be most appropriate to begin your article? Choose one set or words and phrases from options i)-iv).

    i)   good evening / I welcome you on behalf of my school / today I would like to talk about

    ii)   homework is an important issue / I believe that / should pupils be given less homework?

    iii)   hiya / people who don't agree are idiots / my mum says this as well

    iv)   would like to describe / the aim of this article is to give an informative account

  b) Give a reason for your choice, and explain why each of the other options is wrong.

Q2   Fill in the box labelled "words and phrases to begin and end your article" on your planning page.

Q3   *Decide whether you are going to argue that you agree or disagree with homework.*

  a) Read the question again and find two points in the question which support your view. Write them into the box on the planning page labelled "reasons you agree / disagree with homework."

  b) Think of two more reasons why your opinion is right, and write them into the same box.

Q4a) Read the question again, and find two points in the question which disagree with your opinion. Write them into the box labelled "different opinions people might have about homework."

  b) Think of two more reasons why other people might not agree with your opinion and write them into the same box.

Writing — Practice Questions

The Long Writing Question

It's not over yet. More questions about that homework question planning page coming right up...

Q1a) Read through your planning page. Cross out any points which seem unimportant.

b) Number the points you've got in each box in order of how important / good they are. The best point in each box should be number 1.

c) Link together any points which seem similar or related — draw a line between them.

Q2 i) - iii) are all ways you could structure your article but only two of them are good ways. Decide which one would be a bad idea and explain why it's not as good as the others.

i) The reasons why you think your opinion is right go in the first half of the article. In the second half of the article you discuss different points of view people could have and why you think they're wrong.

ii) Each paragraph of your article compares a point for and a point against homework. You argue that the points which agree with your opinion are better.

iii) Each paragraph of your article gives a reason why your point of view is right and backs it up with examples and evidence. This means you don't have to discuss other points of view.

Q3 Is the following statement true or false? Explain your answer.

"It's OK to change your argument halfway through a piece of persuasive writing. Just make sure your conclusion matches the introduction and the examiner won't notice."

Q4 Write a full answer to the exam question on p58. It should cover 1-2 sides of A4.
Pretend you are in the exam, and write the answer in 30 minutes. (30 marks)
Use the planning page you have done to help you.

SAT-STYLE QUESTION

Q5a) When the 30 minutes are up, read through your answer and check the following things:

- ☐ The article has a clear introduction and conclusion.
- ☐ The article is persuasive. It gives good reasons to support one point of view. It acknowledges other points of view exist and gives reasons why they are wrong.
- ☐ The structure of the article is signposted for the reader.
- ☐ The article is written in paragraphs.
- ☐ Interesting vocabulary and sentence structures are used.
- ☐ A range of punctuation is used correctly, e.g. commas, colons, semicolons.
- ☐ The spelling is good.

b) Make any corrections to your answer neatly.

Just put a line through anything you want to change — don't use correction fluid.

The Short Writing Question

The Short Writing Question is worth 20 marks. You only have 30 minutes to plan and write your answer and you <u>don't</u> get a planning page to help you. Here's how to tackle it.

A Case of Mistaken Identity

Your local newspaper is running a story-writing competition for young people:

Young Writers' Story Competition

The theme of this year's competition is mistaken identity.
Write an imaginative story on this topic. You should write about:
- The characters who are mistaken for each other and why they're so alike
- Who mixes them up
- What the result of the mix-up is

The winning entry will be published in the Herald newspaper.

Write your entry to the competition.   *20 marks including 4 marks for spelling*

Q1   Sketch out a grid like this and fill it in.

QUESTION	ANSWER
What is the purpose of this piece of writing?	
Who is going to read it?	
Write down three words which describe the tone you think the writing should have.	

Q2a)   Write down three things that the question tells you should be included in your story.

  b)   Use the three things you know should be included as a way to organise your planning. Write them out as headings on a piece of paper. Then spend 5 minutes brainstorming ideas and scribbling them down under the headings.

Q3   Write a full answer to the question. It should cover just over a side of A4. Pretend you are in the exam, and write your answer in 25 minutes.   (20 marks)
SAT-STYLE QUESTION   Use the plan you have written to help you.

Q4   When you have finished writing, spend a couple of minutes reading through your work and correcting any mistakes.

The section's almost over... keep going... one more...

Don't be scared of writing longer pieces. Planning your answer is the key. If it helps, write down "purpose, tone, structure, paragraphs, interesting sentences" at the top of your plan.

Revision Questions

Q1
SAT-STYLE QUESTION

This is an example of a long writing question. It should take 45 minutes, **including** 15 minutes planning time. Copy out the planning page onto an A4 sheet of paper before you start.

Today's News: Accident at Sporting Event

Write an article for a broadsheet newspaper about an accident at a major sporting event. You should make your account believable, but you do not have to base it on facts.

You should include:
• a headline
• a description of what happened
• quotes from people who witnessed the accident
• information about action which is going to be taken to improve safety in the future

30 marks

Use this page to plan your work.

> a headline for your article

> what happened, when and where

> quotes from people who were there

> what's going to happen next

Q2
SAT-STYLE QUESTION

This is another example of a long writing question.
Copy out the planning page onto an A4 sheet before you start.

Dealing with Bullying in Schools

Your school is trying to tackle bullying.
They want pupils to produce a leaflet on the topic:

Calling All Students

We would like you to produce a leaflet about how students can deal with bullying. It should comment on the advantages and disadvantages of different actions students can take, e.g.
• talking to a teacher
• talking to a friend or parent
• avoiding or ignoring the bullies
• fighting or talking back to the bullies

Write the text for the leaflet.

30 marks

Use this page to plan your work.

> words and phrases to begin and end your discussion

> different ways to deal with bullying

> advantages and disadvantages of each method

Q3
SAT-STYLE QUESTION

Here's an example of a short writing question. Do it in **30 minutes**.

No Shakespeare at Local Theatre

A local theatre has decided to stop putting on Shakespeare's plays.
This is an extract from a letter by an English teacher to the local newspaper:

> **The local theatre has completely failed to see two important points:**
> 1. **Shakespeare's plays are not boring; they are filled with humour, suspense and drama.**
> 2. **Students in local schools studying the plays gain a lot from seeing them performed.**

As a Year 9 pupil, write a letter to the managing director of the local theatre, Marcus Straw, arguing that Shakespeare's plays should still be performed there. You don't need to include an address.

20 marks including 4 marks for spelling

Know Your Play

You **have** to know the story of your play and a few basics about all the characters. If you don't you'll be very stuck on the day of the SAT. Do these questions and **learn** the answers.

Q1a) Write a one or two sentence summary of each **scene** in your play.

b) Write a one or two sentence summary of each **act** in your play.

You'll only have to write about certain bits of the play — these are your <u>set scenes</u>.
If you don't know which scenes they are, then ask your teacher <u>right now</u>.

Q2a) Write a detailed summary of your set scenes.

b) Draw a storyboard for each of your set scenes.

It doesn't have to be fine art — just draw matchstick figures. The point is to get a clear picture of who's talking to who and what they're doing.

Q3 Sketch out a grid like this and fill it in for all the characters that appear in your set scenes.

Name	Job or title	Age	Appearance	Personality	Quotes
Leonato	Governor of Messina	Middle-aged (Hero's his daughter)	Respectable-looking — probably well-dressed	Usually friendly, but has a temper	"Death is the fairest cover for her shame / That may be wish'd for."

e.g.

Q4 Copy out the list of themes for the play you're studying.
Write down as many quotes as you can from your set scenes that are linked to the themes.

RICHARD III

Good and evil

Crimes

Guilt

Loyalty

Dreams and omens

MUCH ADO ABOUT NOTHING

True love

Tricks

Honour

Appearances

THE TEMPEST

Fate and justice

Magic

Freedom

Betrayal

Forgiveness

Q5 Write down a one sentence definition for each of these words. If you don't know the answer look it up in a dictionary and rewrite the definition in your own words.

a) act
b) scene
c) character

d) tragedy
e) comedy
f) history play

g) line
h) speech
i) phrase

j) prose
k) poetry
l) metre

m) exit
n) exeunt
o) aside

Understanding the Language

The hardest thing about Shakespeare is understanding the language. You can learn some of the tricky words in advance, but it's best if you know how to <u>work out</u> what odd words mean, too.

Q1   The words on the left pop up all the time in Shakespeare. Write each of them out next to their modern meanings from the box on the right.

Make sure you do all 12.

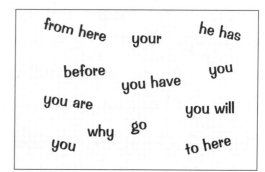

Q2   Write down what you think each highlighted word means.

a)

> LEONATO   Indeed he looks younger than he did, by the loss of a beard.
>
> PEDRO   Nay, 'a rubs himself with civet. Can you smell him out by that?
>
> **Much Ado About Nothing**, Act 3 Scene 2, lines 44-47

Don't panic if you see a word you don't know — try and work it out.

b)

> PROSPERO   O Ferdinand!
> Do not smile at me that I boast her off,
> For thou shalt find she will outstrip all praise,
> And make it halt behind her.
>
> **The Tempest**, Act 4 Scene 1, lines 8-11

c)

> LOVELL   Come, come, dispatch. 'Tis bootless to exclaim.
>
> HASTINGS   O bloody Richard! Miserable England!
> I prophesy the fearfull'st time to thee
> That ever wretched age hath looked upon.
>
> **Richard III**, Act 3 Scene 4, lines 101-104

d)

> RICHARD   Stay, you that bear that corse, and set it down.
>
> ANNE   What black magician conjures up this fiend
> To stop devoted charitable deeds?
>
> RICHARD   Villains, set down the corse, or, by Saint Paul,
> I'll make a corse of him that disobeys!
>
> FIRST GENTLEMAN   My lord, stand back, and let the coffin pass.
>
> **Richard III**, Act 1 Scene 2, lines 33-38

Understanding the Language

If you've got a rough idea what the characters are going on about, you're doing pretty well.
A good way to test whether you really understand is to put what they say into your own words.

Q1   Write this speech out in your own words.

> HASTINGS   Woe, woe for England! Not a whit for me —
> For I, too fond, might have prevented this.
> Stanley did dream the boar did raze our helms;
> And I did scorn it and disdain to fly.
> Three times today my foot-cloth horse did stumble,
> And started when he looked upon the Tower,
> As loath to bear me to the slaughter-house.
> ### *Richard III*, Act 3 Scene 4, lines 79-85

If there's a bit you don't get, have a guess at what it might mean.

Q2   Write this speech out in simple, modern language.

> BENEDICK   O, she misused me past the endurance of a block!
> An oak but with one green leaf on it would have answered her; my
> very visor began to assume life and scold with her. She told me,
> not thinking I had been myself, that I was the Prince's jester, that I
> was duller than a great thaw; huddling jest upon jest with such
> impossible conveyance upon me that I stood like a man at a mark,
> with a whole army shooting at me. She speaks poniards and every
> word stabs. If her breath were as terrible as her terminations, there
> were no living near her — she would infect to the north star. I
> would not marry her, though she were endowed with all that Adam
> had left him before he transgressed.
> ### *Much Ado About Nothing*, Act 2 Scene 1, lines 211-221

Shut yer trap.

Q3   You know what I'm going to say... Yep, write this speech out in your own words.

> PROSPERO   Behold, Sir King,
> The wronged Duke of Milan, Prospero.
> For more assurance that a living prince
> Does now speak to thee, I embrace thy body,
> And to thee and thy company I bid
> A hearty welcome.
> ### *The Tempest*, Act 5 Scene 1, lines 106-111

Q4   Choose an extract from your set scenes that's at least 15 lines long. Write it out in your own words.

If you're still not sure which are your set scenes, then find out from your teacher now.

Shakespeare — The Basics

Backing Up Your Answers

You can have the world's brainiest ideas in your Shakespeare answer in the SAT, but you'll only get about half the marks if you don't back them up with quotes.

Q1   Look at each bit of text. Find the exact words which back up the statement on the right and write them down.

You don't need to explain your answers for now — just write out the bits of text you'll need.

a)
> RICHARD   But he, poor man, by your first order died,
> And that a winged Mercury did bear;
> Some tardy cripple bore the countermand,
> That came too lag to see him buried.
>
> **Richard III, Act 2 Scene 1, lines 88-91**

Richard pretends to be sad that Clarence is dead.

What does Richard say to suggest he feels sorry for Clarence?

b)
> DON JOHN   I had rather be a canker in a hedge than a rose in his grace, and it better fits my blood to be disdained of all than to fashion a carriage to rob love from any. In this, though I cannot be said to be a flattering honest man, it must not be denied but I am a plain-dealing villain.
>
> **Much Ado About Nothing, Act 1 Scene 3, lines 25-29**

Don John openly admits that he is evil.

There's one phrase that really sums up how Don John feels about himself.

c)
> PROSPERO   For you, most wicked sir, whom to call brother
> Would even infect my mouth, I do forgive
> Thy rankest fault — all of them — and require
> My dukedom of thee, which perforce I know
> Thou must restore.
>
> **The Tempest, Act 5 Scene 1, lines 130-134**

Prospero should sound angry with Antonio, even though he forgives him.

These ones are a bit different. Imagine you've made these points, and try to back them up.

d)
> MARGARET   O princely Buckingham, I'll kiss thy hand
> In sign of league and amity with thee:
> Now fair befall thee and thy noble House!
> Thy garments are not spotted with our blood,
> Nor thou within the compass of my curse.
>
> **Richard III, Act 1 Scene 3, lines 279-283**

Queen Margaret could point at Buckingham's clothes at this point.

e)
> PROSPERO   you demi-puppets that
> By moonshine do the green sour ringlets make,
> Whereof the ewe not bites; and you whose pastime
> Is to make midnight mushrooms, that rejoice
> To hear the solemn curfew; by whose aid —
> Weak masters though ye be — I have bedimmed
> The noontide sun, called forth the mutinous winds,
> And 'twixt the green sea and the azured vault
> Set roaring war.
>
> **The Tempest, Act 5 Scene 1, lines 36-44**

Prospero shows how powerful his magic is by using lots of natural imagery.

You can't just quote one bit — you'll have to quote a few.

Backing Up Your Answers

... more practice at finding words from the text to prove your ideas are the product of full-blown genius.

Q1   Find the words in each piece of text which back up the statement to the right.

a)
TYRREL   Let me have open means to come to them,
And soon I'll rid you from the fear of them.

RICHARD   Thou sing'st sweet music. Hark, come hither, Tyrrel.
Go by this token. Rise, and lend thine ear.
Richard III, Act 4 Scene 2, lines 75-78

> Richard should hand something to Tyrrel as he speaks.

Find the words that suggest he gives something to Tyrrel.

b)
CALIBAN   Why, as I told thee, 'tis a custom with him
I' th' afternoon to sleep. There thou mayst brain him,
Having first seized his books, or with a log
Batter his skull, or paunch him with a stake,
Or cut his wezand with thy knife. Remember
First to possess his books
The Tempest, Act 3 Scene 2, lines 87-92

> Caliban wants Prospero's death to be painful and violent.

Find the different ways that Caliban suggests Stephano should kill Prospero.

c)
DOGBERRY   Is our whole dissembly appeared?

VERGES   O, a stool and a cushion for the Sexton.

SEXTON   Which be the malefactors?

DOGBERRY   Marry, that am I and my partner.

VERGES   Nay, that's certain. We have the exhibition to examine.

SEXTON   But which are the offenders that are to be examined?
Let them come before master constable.

DOGBERRY   Yea, marry, let them come before me.
Much Ado About Nothing, Act 4 Scene 2, lines 1-9

> The humour in this scene comes from the Watch's comical attempts to use long, clever words.

You need to find the long words that they use wrongly.

d)
CLAUDIO   There, Leonato, take her back again:
Give not this rotten orange to your friend —
She's but the sign and semblance of her honour.
Behold how like a maid she blushes here!
O, what authority and show of truth
Can cunning sin cover itself withal!
Comes not that blood as modest evidence
To witness simple virtue? Would you not swear,
All you that see her, that she were a maid,
By these exterior shows? But she is none:
She knows the heat of a luxurious bed,
Her blush is guiltiness, not modesty.
Much Ado About Nothing, Act 4 Scene 1, lines 31-42

> Claudio is completely taken in by Don John's trick, and is extremely cruel to Hero.

You can back this point up by quoting his accusations and his insulting descriptions of her.

Writing Your Answers

You make your point and you find a quote to back it up. Then you've got to <u>explain</u> how the quote backs up your comment. It shouldn't be too hard — just don't forget to do it.

Q1 *Here's something a bit easier to read as a break from all that Shakespeare.*

> There once was a playwright called Kit
> Who wrote hit after hit after hit.
> Each day he used up forty goose-feather quills;
> Lords, ladies and gents all rated his skills —
> But the geese didn't like him one bit.

a) Work through these questions, then put your answers together to give a full answer to the question in the box.

   i) Was Kit's work successful in the theatre, yes or no?

   ii) Which words tell you this?

   iii) Explain why these words show the work was successful.

> **According to the limerick, was Kit's work popular?**

b) Work through these questions, then put your answers together to give a full answer to the question in the box.

   i) Which words tell you that people thought that Kit was talented?

   ii) What effects does the writer use, e.g. colourful adjectives, rhetorical question, repetition...?

   iii) How do the effects that the writer uses add to the impression that people thought Kit talented?

> **How does the writer emphasise Kit's popularity?**

c) Now answer this question fully, including your main point, a quote and an explanation.

> **Why didn't the geese like Kit?**

Q2 Read this review and answer the question to the right.

(6 marks)

> Last night's performance of *Richard III* was like a grand opera and a fireworks display rolled into one. Luke Matchett *lived* the title role and Fiona Dunn's Queen Margaret was suitably evil, whilst hinting at an underlying sadness. An absolute triumph!

> **How does the writer emphasise her opinion about the performance?**

Use parts a)-c) above to help you plan your answer. Back up your answer with quotes and explanations.

Writing Your Answers

You're on your own now, sunshine. Well, not quite alone. You've got all these lovely questions here to keep you company. Lucky you. Lucky, lucky, lucky you. Don't forget those quotes...

Q1 *Answer each question in turn. When you make a point, remember to back it up with a quote and explain how the point goes with your quote.*

> BEATRICE   I wonder that you will still be talking, Signior Benedick. Nobody marks you.
>
> BENEDICK   What, my dear Lady Disdain — are you yet living?
>
> BEATRICE   Is it possible disdain should die while she hath such meet food to feed it as Signior Benedick? Courtesy itself must convert to disdain, if you come in her presence.
>
> BENEDICK   Then is courtesy a turncoat. But it is certain I am loved of all ladies — only you excepted — and I would I could find in my heart that I had not a hard heart, for, truly, I love none.
>
> BEATRICE   A dear happiness to women, they would else have been troubled with a pernicious suitor. I thank God and my cold blood, I am of your humour for that — I had rather hear my dog bark at a crow than a man swear he loves me.
>
> BENEDICK   God keep your ladyship still in that mind so some gentleman or other shall scape a predestinate scratched face.
>
> BEATRICE   Scratching could not make it worse, an 'twere such a face as yours were.
>
> BENEDICK   Well, you are a rare parrot-teacher.
>
> BEATRICE   A bird of my tongue is better than a beast of yours.
>
> BENEDICK   I would my horse had the speed of your tongue, and so good a continuer. But keep your way, i' God's name — I have done.
>
> BEATRICE   You always end with a jade's trick. I know you of old.
>
> ***Much Ado About Nothing**, Act 1 Scene 1, lines 107-124*

pernicious
= nasty.

a) What impression does this extract give you of Benedick and Beatrice's relationship?

b) Sketch out the grid below, then fill it in with quotes to back up each point.

Point	Quote
Beatrice suggests people find Benedick boring.	
Beatrice says she never wants to get married.	
Benedick says Beatrice would be violent towards a husband.	
Benedick says Beatrice just repeats old sayings she's learnt.	

c) What kind of atmosphere is there in this scene?

Don't answer back — always answer forwards...

So, that's the basics of how to answer the questions. The next twenty pages or so are all about the different kinds of question you could get in the SAT. Twenty pages of unfettered joy. Sigh.

What Characters Do

When you get a 'character' question in the SATs — and you never know what you're going to get — the best place to start is by having a general look at what the characters **do**.

Q1   *This is what the main characters get up to in some early scenes of three Shakespeare plays.*

Richard III — *RICHARD*

> ACT 1 SCENE 1 Richard says his deformed appearance is better suited to being a villain than doing good, and says he has set King Edward and Clarence against each other.
>
> ACT 1 SCENE 2 Richard convinces Anne to marry him despite admitting killing her husband and father-in-law.
>
> ACT 1 SCENE 3 Richard gives instructions for the murder of his brother Clarence.

Much Ado About Nothing — *CLAUDIO*

> ACT 1 SCENE 1 A messenger describes Claudio's bravery in the war. Claudio has fallen in love with Hero, and Don Pedro says he'll set them up.
>
> ACT 2 SCENE 1 Claudio is tricked by Don John into thinking Don Pedro is after Hero for himself.
>
> ACT 3 SCENE 2 Claudio is again fooled by Don John, this time into thinking Hero's been unfaithful.

The Tempest — *PROSPERO*

> ACT 1 SCENE 2 Prospero tells Miranda he raised the storm with his magic. He is angry with Ariel when he complains about being given more work to do. Prospero threatens to torture Caliban if he doesn't do his tasks. Prospero is pleased when Miranda and Ferdinand fall in love but wants to test how strong their love is.
>
> ACT 3 SCENE 1 Prospero is pleased as he sees how much Miranda and Ferdinand are in love.

good with words   awkward   cunning   gullible   caring   ruthless

powerful   invincible   has a temper   useless   has a good reputation

a) Write out at least two of the words or phrases above to describe Richard, Claudio and Prospero.

b) Write a sentence to explain why you've chosen each word or phrase.

Q2   *Read this extract, then answer the questions.*

> RICHARD   Come hither, Catesby. Rumour it abroad
> That Anne, my wife, is very grievous sick;
> I will take order for her keeping close.
> Inquire me out some mean poor gentleman,
> Whom I will marry straight to Clarence' daughter.
> The boy is foolish, and I fear not him.
> Look how thou dream'st!
> **Richard III, Act 4 Scene 2, lines 49-55**

a) Write these sentences out in the order of the speech above so they describe Richard's plans.

"Find a commoner to marry Clarence's daughter."   *"Spread a rumour that Anne is seriously ill."*

"Stop messing about!"   *"I'll make sure Anne doesn't go anywhere."*

b) Write a few sentences explaining what this extract tells you about Richard's character.

What Characters Say

Almost everything a character says tells you a bit more about them.
Here's some more practice at working out what characters are like and writing about it.

Q1 *These extracts are both from speeches Benedick makes in* Much Ado About Nothing.

In this extract, Benedick's just been tricked into thinking Beatrice is in love with him.

A That a woman conceived me, I thank her; that she brought me up, I likewise give her most humble thanks: but that I will have a recheat winded in my forehead, or hang my bugle in an invisible baldrick, all women shall pardon me.
Much Ado About Nothing, Act 1 Sc 1, 221-225

B Shall quips and sentences and these paper bullets of the brain awe a man from the career of his humour? No, the world must be peopled.
Much Ado About Nothing, Act 2 Sc 3, 228-230

a) Say which of the extracts each of these sentences is about.

Benedick says that you shouldn't be held to things you've said in the past.

Benedick says he'll never get married.

b) Which speech shows Benedick is proud? Explain why.

c) Which speech shows Benedick isn't as sure of himself as he'd like to be? Explain why.

Q2 *These two bits are from speeches made by Prospero in* The Tempest.

A A treacherous army levied, one midnight
Fated to th' purpose, did Antonio open
The gates of Milan, and i' th' dead of darkness,
The ministers for th' purpose hurried thence
Me and thy crying self.
The Tempest, Act 1 Scene 2, lines 128-132

B You, brother mine, that entertained ambition,
Expelled remorse and nature, who, with Sebastian —
Whose inward pinches therefore are most strong —
Would here have killed your king, I do forgive thee,
Unnatural though thou art.
The Tempest, Act 5 Scene 1, lines 75-79

a) Say which of the extracts each of these sentences is about.

Prospero says he forgives Antonio and Sebastian for betraying him and plotting against Alonso.

Prospero talks about how he and Miranda were banished from Milan.

b) Write down three words you could use to describe Prospero as he appears in these quotes.

Q3 *These words are spoken by Richard towards the end of* Richard III.

A Go, gentlemen, every man unto his charge.
Let not our babbling dreams affright our souls.
Richard III, Act 5 Scene 3, lines 308-309

B Our ancient word of courage, fair Saint George,
Inspire us with the spleen of fiery dragons!
Upon them! Victory sits on our helms.
Richard III, Act 5 Scene 3, lines 350-352

a) In your own words, write out what Richard's saying in each speech.

Just base your answer on these two extracts.

b) Write down at least three words you could use to describe Richard.

What Characters Say

For a really good 'character' answer you need to go into quite a bit of detail about the way the characters speak and how they treat each other.

You'll be able to answer the questions on this page even if you don't know the plays.

Q1   *Read the extract then answer the questions.*

King Alonso and his followers have just been washed up on an island after their ship was caught in a storm. Alonso fears his son Ferdinand is dead, but Gonzalo has been trying to comfort him.

> ALONSO   You cram these words into mine ears against
> The stomach of my sense. Would I had never
> Married my daughter there, for, coming thence,
> My son is lost, and, in my rate, she too,
> Who is so far from Italy removed
> I ne'er again shall see her. O thou mine heir
> Of Naples and of Milan, what strange fish
> Hath made his meal on thee?
>
> **The Tempest, Act 2 Scene 1, lines 104-111**

a)   Write out each of these comments about Alonso with the best explanation from the box.

   i)   Alonso is pessimistic.

   ii)   Alonso feels guilty.

   iii) Alonso is irritable.

> • He's annoyed when people try to cheer him up.
> • He blames himself for what's happened to Ferdinand.
> • He feels sure Ferdinand is dead.

b)   Write down a quote from the extract to back up each of the explanations from part a).

Q2   *Read the extract then answer the questions.*

King Richard wants the young Princes dead, as they are a threat to his position.

> RICHARD   Shall I be plain? I wish the bastards dead,
> And I would have it suddenly performed.
> What sayest thou now? Speak suddenly, be brief.
>
> BUCKINGHAM   Your Grace may do your pleasure.
>
> RICHARD   Tut, tut, thou art all ice; thy kindness freezes.
> Say, have I thy consent that they shall die?
>
> BUCKINGHAM   Give me some little breath, some pause, dear lord,
> Before I positively speak in this;
> I will resolve you herein presently.
>
> **Richard III, Act 4 Scene 2, lines 18-26**

a)   Write out each of these comments about the characters' feelings with the best explanation from the box.

   i)   Richard doesn't feel bad about killing the Princes.

   ii)   Buckingham is unsure about Richard's request.

   iii) Richard is impatient with Buckingham.

> • Richard repeats his question to Buckingham.
> • Buckingham asks for some time to think.
> • Richard openly states his plans.

b)   Write down quotes from the extract to back up each of the explanations from part a).

What Characters Say

It's all about <u>backing up</u> your answer. You can say Macbeth and Beatrice were turquoise unicorns with an unhealthy obsession with candyfloss — so long as you can back it up with evidence...

Q1   Read the piece of text, then sketch out the table and fill in the missing explanations and quotes.

> BEATRICE   What fire is in mine ears? Can this be true?
> Stand I condemned for pride and scorn so much?
> Contempt, farewell, and maiden pride, adieu!
> No glory lives behind the back of such.
> And, Benedick, love on. I will requite thee,
> Taming my wild heart to thy loving hand.
> If thou dost love, my kindness shall incite thee
> To bind our loves up in a holy band;
> For others say thou dost deserve, and I
> Believe it better than reportingly.
> ***Much Ado About Nothing***, Act 3 Scene 1, lines 108-117

Comment	Explanation	Quote
Beatrice cares about what people think of her.	She decides to change the way she acts after people criticise her.	"Contempt, farewell, and maiden pride, adieu!"
She feels bad for the way she's treated Benedick.		
She's not as clever as she thinks she is.		

Q2   Read the extract below, then sketch a grid like the one from Q1 and fill in as many comments, backed up by quotes and explanations, as you can.

> PROSPERO Thou poisonous slave, got by the devil himself
> Upon thy wicked dam, come forth!
> *Enter* CALIBAN
> CALIBAN As wicked dew as e'er my mother brushed
> With raven's feather from unwholesome fen
> Drop on you both! A south-west blow on ye
> And blister you all o'er!
> PROSPERO For this, be sure, tonight thou shalt have cramps,
> Side-stitches that shall pen thy breath up, urchins
> Shall, for that vast of night that they may work,
> All exercise on thee, thou shalt be pinched
> As thick as honeycomb, each pinch more stinging
> Than bees that made 'em.

> CALIBAN   I must eat my dinner.
> This island's mine, by Sycorax my mother,
> Which thou tak'st from me. When thou cam'st first,
> Thou strok'st me and made much of me, wouldst give me
> Water with berries in't, and teach me how
> To name the bigger light, and how the less,
> That burn by day and night, and then I loved thee,
> And showed thee all the qualities o'th'isle,
> The fresh springs, brine-pits, barren place and fertile.
>
> Cursed be I that did so! All the charms
> Of Sycorax, toads, beetles, bats, light on you!
> ***The Tempest***, Act 1 Scene 2, lines 321-342

Q3   Choose a character who's in all your set scenes. Write an essay explaining what we learn about the character in the scenes.   (18 marks)

SAT-STYLE QUESTION

Don't forget to explain your points and back them up with quotes.

How Characters Think

For these questions you have to work out why the character acts a particular way.

Q1   *In this extract from* The Tempest, *Prospero gives his slave Caliban some instructions.*

> PROSPERO   Hag-seed, hence!
> Fetch us in fuel. And be quick, thou 'rt best,
> To answer other business. Shrugg'st thou, malice?
> If thou neglect'st, or dost unwillingly
> What I command, I'll rack thee with old cramps,
> Fill all thy bones with aches, make thee roar,
> That beasts shall tremble at thy din.
> CALIBAN   No, pray thee.
> *(aside)* I must obey. His art is of such power,
> It would control my dam's god, Setebos,
> And make a vassal of him.
> **The Tempest, Act 1 Scene 2, lines 367-376**

rack = torture

art = magic

vassal = inferior person

a)   What does Prospero tell Caliban to do?

b)   Why does Prospero become annoyed with Caliban?

c)   Why does Caliban decide to do as he is told?

Q2   Below are three quotes from Hastings in *Richard III*. Match each one to the correct summary.

> **A** Tell him his fears are shallow, without instance;
> And for his dreams, I wonder he's so simple
> To trust the mockery of unquiet slumbers.
> **Richard III, Act 3 Scene 2, lines 25-27**

> **B** But I shall laugh at this a twelve-month hence,
> That they which brought me in my master's hate,
> I live to look upon their tragedy.
> **Richard III, Act 3 Scene 2, lines 57-59**

> **C** Think you, but that I know our state secure,
> I would be so triumphant as I am?
> **Richard III, Act 3 Scene 2, lines 81-82**

i)   Hastings says he wouldn't act so assured if he wasn't certain of his safety.

ii) Hastings says Stanley is silly to be worried.

iii) Hastings gloats over what has happened to his enemies.

Q3   Read the extract from *Much Ado About Nothing* then answer the questions below.

> BENEDICK *(coming forward)* This can be no trick. The conference was sadly borne. They have the truth of this from Hero. They seem to pity the lady: it seems her affections have their full bent. Love me! Why, it must be requited. I hear how I am censured.
> **Much Ado About Nothing, Act 2 Scene 3, lines 210-214**

Don Pedro, Leonato and Claudio have just been playing a trick on Benedick by saying that Beatrice is in love with him, while they know he is listening in to their conversation.

censured = criticised

a)   Why is Benedick convinced he is not being tricked?

b)   The other characters criticise Benedick. What effect does this have on him?
     Explain your answer.

Writing About Descriptions

You won't have to write a whole essay on description — but try to mention it in any language task.

Q1   *In this bit from* Much Ado About Nothing, *Claudio describes how he fell in love with Hero.*

> CLAUDIO   O, my lord,
> When you went onward on this ended action,
> I looked upon her with a soldier's eye,
> That liked, but had a rougher task in hand
> Than to drive liking to the name of love;
> But now I am returned and that war-thoughts
> Have left their places vacant, in their rooms
> Come thronging soft and delicate desires,
> All prompting me how fair young Hero is,
> Saying I liked her ere I went to wars.
>
> ***Much Ado About Nothing*, Act 1 Scene 1, lines 274-283**

ended action =
the war they've
just won

rougher task = fighting

ere = before

a) Write these events out in the order they happened.

Claudio went to fight in the war.	*He liked Hero but didn't fall in love with her.*	*Claudio saw Hero for the first time.*	*Claudio fell in love with Hero.*	*After the war ended he had more time to think about love.*

b) Write down two phrases which show how Claudio was feeling before he went to war.

c) Write down one phrase which shows how Claudio is feeling now.

d) Explain how Claudio uses the image of "rooms" to describe how his feelings changed.

e) Write a mini-essay explaining how the language of this piece creates a clear   **(8 marks)**
    picture of what's happened. Include information from your answers to a) to d).
    SAT-STYLE QUESTION

Q2   Write a mini-essay explaining how the language in this bit from   **(8 marks)**
SAT-STYLE QUESTION   *Richard III* creates a clear picture of Richard's past behaviour.

> ANNE   Foul devil, for God's sake hence, and trouble us not,
> For thou hast made the happy earth thy hell,
> Filled it with cursing cries and deep exclaims.
> If thou delight to view thy heinous deeds,
> Behold this pattern of thy butcheries.
> O gentlemen, see! See dead Henry's wounds
> Open their congealed mouths and bleed afresh!
> Blush, blush, thou lump of foul deformity;
> For 'tis thy presence that exhales this blood
> From cold and empty veins where no blood dwells.
> Thy deeds inhuman and unnatural
> Provokes this deluge most unnatural.
>
> ***Richard III*, Act 1 Scene 2, lines 50-61**

Writing About Imagery

If you're writing about language and you spot some imagery, __definitely__ mention it.
It'll go down a treat with the examiners.

Q1   *For each extract below, answer the questions that follow.*

A   BENEDICK   She speaks poniards and every word stabs.
Much Ado About Nothing, Act 2 Scene 1, line 222

poniard = dagger

B   QUEEN MARGARET   Why strew'st thou sugar on that bottled spider
Whose deadly web ensnareth thee about?
Richard III, Act 1 Scene 3, lines 241-242

C   *Caliban, Stephano and Trinculo are driven out*
PROSPERO   Go charge my goblins that they grind their joints
With dry convulsions, shorten up their sinews
With aged cramps, and more pinch-spotted make them
Than pard or cat o' mountain.
The Tempest, Act 4 Scene 1, lines 257-260

Prospero is telling Ariel to use magic to torment Caliban, Stephano and Trinculo, who have been plotting against Prospero.

pard = leopard

cat o' mountain = another word for leopard

a)   What's being described in the image?

b)   What's it being compared to?

c)   What does the image tell you about the thing being described?

d)   What does the image tell you about the character's thoughts or state of mind?

It's OK if you only answer e) for the play you're studying.

e)   What does the image add to the overall feel of the play? Explain your answer.

Q2
SAT-STYLE QUESTION
What effect do you think the imagery in this extract from *Richard III* would have on
an audience? Use parts a) to d) from above to help you plan your mini-essay.

(8 marks)

King Richard hired Tyrrel to kill the young Prince Edward and his brother the Duke of York. Here Tyrrel recalls how Dighton and Forrest, who he got to kill the Princes, described them just before they were killed.

TYRREL   'Thus, thus,' quoth Forrest, 'girdling one another
Within their alabaster innocent arms.
Their lips were four red roses on a stalk,
And in their summer beauty kissed each other.
A book of prayers on their pillow lay,
Which once,' quoth Forrest, 'almost changed my mind.
But O, the Devil —'
Richard III, Act 4 Scene 3, lines 10-16

quoth = said

alabaster = white

Writing About the Mood

Mood means the atmosphere the language creates and how it makes the audience feel.

Q1   Read the extracts, then sketch out and fill in the table below.

	Setting	How the characters speak	Description & imagery	MOOD
A				
B				

A

CALIBAN How does thy honour? Let me lick thy shoe.
I'll not serve him — he is not valiant.
TRINCULO Thou liest, most ignorant monster: I am in case to jostle a constable. Why, thou debauched fish, thou, was there ever man a coward that hath drunk so much sack as I today? Wilt thou tell a monstrous lie, being but half a fish and half a monster?
CALIBAN Lo, how he mocks me! Wilt thou let him, my lord?
TRINCULO 'Lord' quoth he! That a monster should be such a natural!
CALIBAN Lo, lo again! Bite him to death, I prithee.
The Tempest, Act 3 Scene 2, lines 22-30

For each note you make, write a quote to show where you got your idea from.

natural = idiot

canker = a wild flower that was treated as a weed

blood = temper

enfranchised with a clog = set free from imprisonment, but with a ball and chain (so not truly free)

B

DON JOHN   I had rather be a canker in a hedge than a rose in his grace, and it better fits my blood to be disdained of all than to fashion a carriage to rob love from any. In this, though I cannot be said to be a flattering honest man, it must not be denied but I am a plain-dealing villain. I am trusted with a muzzle and enfranchised with a clog; therefore I have decreed not to sing in my cage. If I had my mouth, I would bite; if I had my liberty, I would do my liking. In the meantime let me be that I am and seek not to alter me.
Much Ado About Nothing, Act 1 Scene 3, lines 25-31

C

ELIZABETH My Lord of Gloucester, I have too long borne
Your blunt upbraidings and your bitter scoffs;
By heaven, I will acquaint his Majesty
Of those gross taunts that oft I have endured.
I had rather be a country servant maid,
Than a great queen, with this condition,
To be so baited, scorned, and stormed at:
        Enter QUEEN MARGARET *behind*
Small joy have I in being England's queen.
MARGARET *(aside)* And lessened be that small, God I beseech him:
Thy honour, state, and seat is due to me.
RICHARD What, threat you me with telling of the King?
Tell him, and spare not: look what I have said
I will avouch 't in presence of the King:
I dare adventure to be sent to th'Tower;
'Tis time to speak: my pains are quite forgot.
MARGARET *(aside)* Out, devil! I do remember them too well:
Thou kill'dst my husband Henry in the Tower,
And Edward, my poor son, at Tewkesbury.
Richard III, Act 1 Scene 3, lines 102-119

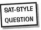
SAT-STYLE QUESTION

Q2   Write a mini-essay on the mood in one of the extracts, using your notes from Q1.   (8 marks)

Writing About Persuasive Language

Examiners love it when you write about persuasive language. Shakespeare uses lots of tricks you can look out for.

Q1   Write down a quote from the extract to show where each of the persuading tricks is being used.

Antonio is trying to persuade Sebastian to kill Alonso and Gonzalo so that Sebastian can take his place as King of Naples.

ANTONIO   Twenty consciences
That stand 'twixt me and Milan, candied be they,
And melt, ere they molest! Here lies your brother,
No better than the earth he lies upon,
If he were that which now he's like — that's dead —
Whom I with this obedient steel, three inches of it,
Can lay to bed for ever, whiles you, doing thus,
To the perpetual wink for aye might put
This ancient morsel, this Sir Prudence, who
Should not upbraid our course. For all the rest,
They'll take suggestion as a cat laps milk,
They'll tell the clock to any business that
We say befits the hour.

The Tempest, Act 2 Scene 1, lines 277-289

Persuading tricks

says it will be very simple to kill Alonso

scoffs at the idea of feeling guilty

says Gonzalo won't be a problem

says no one else will stand in their way

Q2   Write down a quote from the extract to show where each of the persuading tricks is being used.

King Richard is delivering his oration to his troops before they go into battle with Richmond's army, who have come over from France.

RICHARD   Let's whip these stragglers o'er the seas again,
Lash hence these overweening rags of France,
These famished beggars, weary of their lives —
Who, but for dreaming on this fond exploit,
For want of means, poor rats, had hanged themselves.
If we be conquered, let men conquer us!
And not these bastard Bretons, whom our fathers
Have in their own land beaten, bobbed, and thumped,
And in record left them the heirs of shame.
Shall these enjoy our lands? Lie with our wives?
Ravish our daughters?

Richard III, Act 5 Scene 3, lines 328-338

Persuading tricks

uses rhetorical questions

talks about past successes

uses violent language to get soldiers ready for battle

insults their enemies

plays on fears of defeat

uses patriotic language to motivate soldiers

Q3   Write a mini-essay on how persuasive tricks are used in one of the extracts above.   (12 marks)

SAT-STYLE QUESTION

Art thou afeard o' the dreaded SAT?

Mentioning persuasive language in SAT questions will make the examiner as happy as an aardvark wearing ant-infested pants. Point out any persuasive bits and say <u>how</u> they persuade the audience.

Revision Questions — Richard III

This page mixes up a few of the topics from this section.

How does the language add to the hostile atmosphere of these lines?

RICHARD   Have done thy charm, thou hateful withered hag!
MARGARET   And leave out thee? Stay, dog, for thou shalt hear me.
If heaven have any grievous plague in store
Exceeding those that I can wish upon thee,
O, let them keep it till thy sins be ripe,
And then hurl down their indignation
On thee, the troubler of the poor world's peace.
The worm of conscience still begnaw thy soul;
Thy friends suspect for traitors while thou liv'st,
And take deep traitors for thy dearest friends!
No sleep close up that deadly eye of thine,
Unless it be while some tormenting dream
Affrights thee with a hell of ugly devils.
Thou elvish-marked, abortive, rooting hog,
Thou that wast sealed in thy nativity
The slave of nature, and the son of hell;
Thou slander of thy heavy mother's womb,
Thou loathed issue of thy father's loins,
Thou rag of honour, thou detested —
RICHARD   Margaret!
MARGARET   Richard!
RICHARD   Ha?
MARGARET   I call thee not.
RICHARD   I cry thee mercy then, for I did think
That thou hadst called me all these bitter names.

***Richard III*, Act 1 Scene 3, lines 214-235**

Queen Margaret has a go at Richard and Queen Elizabeth, saying they're fighting over what's hers.

elvish-marked = marked by elves at birth

abortive = deformed because of a premature birth

Q1a)   Write down any words or phrases that look like they've got something to do with the question.

b)   Looking at the extract, have a go at answering each of these questions. Don't forget to quote.

Ask yourself these things on __any__ language question.

   i)   What do the different characters think and feel?
   ii)   Are there any descriptive bits? What effect do they have?
   iii)   Is there any imagery used? If so, what does it add to the passage?
   iv)   Are most of the sentences long or short?
   v)   Is the rhythm quick and choppy or slow and steady?

These two can have a big effect on how exciting / magical / confusing the atmosphere of a scene is.

c)   Look back at your answers to a). If you haven't got a comment for each of the quotes, think about how it links to the question now, and write it down.

d)   Plan a full answer to the question at the top of the page, using your answers to a) - c).

e)   Use all your notes to write out a full answer to the question at the top of the page.   (18 marks)

SAT-STYLE QUESTION

Shakespeare — Language Questions

Revision Questions — The Tempest & Much Ado

Two more big fat questions. Use parts a) to d) from page 79 to break them up into nicer chunks.

Q1 | How does the language in this extract create a mood of mystery and magic? | (18 marks)

SAT-STYLE QUESTION

PROSPERO   *(drawing a magic circle on the ground)*
Ye elves of hills, brooks, standing lakes, and groves;
And ye that on the sands with printless foot
Do chase the ebbing Neptune, and do fly him
When he comes back; you demi-puppets that
By moonshine do the green sour ringlets make,
Whereof the ewe not bites; and you whose pastime
Is to make midnight mushrooms, that rejoice
To hear the solemn curfew; by whose aid —
Weak masters though ye be — I have bedimmed
The noontide sun, called forth the mutinous winds,
And 'twixt the green sea and the azured vault
Set roaring war. To the dread rattling thunder
Have I given fire, and rifted Jove's stout oak
With his own bolt; the strong-based promontory
Have I made shake, and by the spurs plucked up
The pine and cedar. Graves at my command
Have waked their sleepers, oped, and let 'em forth,
By my so potent art. But this rough magic
I here abjure, and, when I have required
Some heavenly music — which even now I do —
To work mine end upon their senses that
This airy charm is for, I'll break my staff,
Bury it certain fathoms in the earth,
And deeper than did ever plummet sound
I'll drown my book.   *The Tempest*, Act 5 Scene 1, lines 33-57

Prospero is about to cast one final spell before he gives up his magic.

Neptune = God of the Sea

demi-puppets = fairies

azured vault = blue sky, heaven

promontory = cliff

abjure = give up

Q2 | How does Don Pedro's language create a light-hearted mood in this passage? | (18 marks)

SAT-STYLE QUESTION

DON PEDRO   And Benedick is not the unhopefullest
husband that I know. Thus far can I praise him — he is
of a noble strain, of approved valour and confirmed
honesty. I will teach you how to humour your cousin,
that she shall fall in love with Benedick; and I, with your
two helps, will so practise on Benedick that, in despite of
his quick wit and his queasy stomach, he shall fall in
love with Beatrice. If we can do this, Cupid is no longer
an archer: his glory shall be ours, for we are the only
love-gods. Go in with me, and I will tell you my drift.
    Exeunt

Much Ado About Nothing, Act 2 Scene 1, lines 347-356

Don Pedro, Leonato, Hero and Claudio are planning to trick Benedick and Beatrice into falling in love with each other.

strain = family

in despite = in spite

queasy stomach = easily upset

Cupid = Roman god of love

drift = plan

Name a smoothie playwright — milkshakespeare...

Like a good ice-cream sundae, language questions are usually a bit of a mix. Think about all the topics in this section if you're writing about language. And strawberry sauce. And nuts. Mmm.

Performance — The Basics

For 'performance' questions you normally have to imagine you're the director of the scene. They want you to show that you understand what's going on in the scene and how it could look on stage.

Q1a) Copy out all the bits here where Prospero's talking to himself.

Always ask yourself exactly who the characters are speaking to.

> PROSPERO   Soft, sir, one word more!
> *(Aside)* They are both in either's pow'rs, but this swift business
> I must uneasy make, lest too light winning
> Make the prize light. *(To Ferdinand)* One word more — I
>   charge thee
>
> That thou attend me — thou dost here usurp
> The name thou ow'st not and hast put thyself
> Upon this island as a spy, to win it
> From me, the lord on't.
> **The Tempest,** Act 1 Scene 2, lines 452-459

Prospero's decided to make things difficult for Ferdinand and Miranda, in order to test their love for each other.

Hi! I'm the actor Ben Davis. You may remember me from such films as 'Prospero Saves Christmas' and 'Richard V — The Revenge'.

b) Which of the words on the right describes the way Prospero might talk when he's talking to himself?

c) Which of the words on the right describes the way Prospero might talk when he's talking to Ferdinand?

> thoughtful   forceful   loud
>
>   angry
> accusatory   quiet

Q2   *Characters' feelings often change **during** a scene. Read this extract and look out for changes.*

> DON PEDRO   Well, as time shall try — "In time the savage bull doth bear the yoke."
>
> BENEDICK   The savage bull may — but if ever the sensible Benedick bear it, pluck off the bull's horns and set them in my forehead, and let me be vilely painted, and in such great letters as they write, "Here is good horse to hire" let them signify under my sign "Here you may see Benedick the married man."
>
> CLAUDIO   If this should ever happen, thou wouldst be horn-mad.
>
> DON PEDRO   Nay, if Cupid have not spent all his quiver in Venice, thou wilt quake for this shortly.
>
> BENEDICK   I look for an earthquake too, then.
>
> DON PEDRO   Well, you will temporize with the hours. In the meantime, good Signior Benedick, repair to Leonato's. Commend me to him and tell him I will not fail him at supper; for indeed he hath made great preparation.
>
> BENEDICK   I have almost matter enough in me for such an embassage, and so I commit you —
>
> CLAUDIO   To the tuition of God. From my house, if I had it —
>
> DON PEDRO   The sixth of July. Your loving friend, Benedick.
>
> BENEDICK   Nay, mock not, mock not. The body of your discourse is sometime guarded with fragments, and the guards are but slightly basted on neither. Ere you flout old ends any further, examine your conscience — and so I leave you.   *Exit*
>
> **Much Ado About Nothing,** Act 1 Scene 1, lines 240-254

Explain how and why Benedick's feelings change during this extract.

How Characters Speak

The Number 1 Big Thing to include in 'imagine you're a director' questions is how the characters should <u>sound</u> — what tone of voice they should use, how loudly they speak — that sort of thing.

Q1a) Say how you think Richard feels in each of the highlighted parts of the text.

There's no right or wrong answer to this question.

RICHARD The deep-revolving witty
                               Buckingham
No more shall be the neighbour to my counsels.
Hath he so long held out with me untired,
And stops he now for breath? Well, be it so.
                Enter STANLEY, *Earl of Derby*
How now, Lord Stanley? What's the news?
STANLEY   Know, my loving lord,
The Marquis Dorset, as I hear, is fled
To Richmond, in the parts where he abides.
[Stands aside]
RICHARD Come hither, Catesby. Rumour it abroad
That Anne, my wife, is very grievous sick;
I will take order for her keeping close.

Inquire me out some mean poor gentleman,
Whom I will marry straight to Clarence' daughter.
The boy is foolish, and I fear not him.
Look how thou dream'st! I say again, give out
That Anne, my queen, is sick and like to die.
About it! For it stands me much upon
To stop all hopes whose growth may damage me.
                Exit CATESBY
I must be married to my brother's daughter,
Or else my kingdom stands on brittle glass.
Murder her brothers, and then marry her —
Uncertain way of gain! But I am in
So far in blood that sin will pluck on sin.
Tear-falling pity dwells not in this eye.
                Richard III, Act 4 Scene 2, lines 42-64

b) Suggest what tone of voice the actor could use to emphasise his feelings to the audience when he speaks the highlighted words. Choose from the suggestions below, or use your own ideas.

annoyed   worried   single-minded   angry   commanding   determined

remorseless   assertive   confident   impatient   regretful

Q2
[SAT-STYLE QUESTION]
Suggest how the actor playing Prospero could speak the lines below to emphasise his feelings to the audience.

(12 marks)

PROSPERO   O good Gonzalo,
My true preserver, and a loyal sir
To him thou follow'st! I will pay thy graces
Home both in word and deed. Most cruelly
Didst thou, Alonso, use me and my daughter.
Thy brother was a furtherer in the act. —
Thou art pinched for't now, Sebastian. — Flesh and blood,
You, brother mine, that entertained ambition,
Expelled remorse and nature, who, with Sebastian —
Whose inward pinches therefore are most strong —
Would here have killed your king, I do forgive thee,
Unnatural though thou art. Their understanding
Begins to swell, and the approaching tide
Will shortly fill the reasonable shore
That now lies foul and muddy. Not one of them
That yet looks on me, or would know me. Ariel,
Fetch me the hat and rapier in my cell.
                The Tempest, Act 5 Scene 1, lines 68-84

Detailed answers get good marks. General wishy-washy ones get zilch marks.

rapier = a type of sword

How Characters Move

The second Big Thing to include in 'imagine you're a director' questions is how the characters should <u>move</u>. Movements can emphasise what the characters say and how they react to other characters.

Q1 *Read the extract on the right and answer the questions.*

a) Write out all the bits that tell you how the characters should move and describe the movements in your own words.

b) Write down other possible movements — quote to show **when** the characters should move.

> BUCKINGHAM   Lord mayor —
>
> RICHARD   Look to the drawbridge there!
>
> BUCKINGHAM   Hark! A drum.
>
> RICHARD   Catesby, o'erlook the walls.
>
> BUCKINGHAM   Lord Mayor, the reason we have sent—
>
> RICHARD   Look back, defend thee! Here are enemies!
>
> BUCKINGHAM   God and our innocence defend and guard us!
>
> *Enter* LOVELL *and* RATCLIFFE, *with Hastings' head*
>
> RICHARD   Be patient, they are friends — Ratcliffe and Lovell.
>
> LOVELL   Here is the head of that ignoble traitor,
> The dangerous and unsuspected Hastings.
>
> **Richard III, Act 3 Scene 5, lines 14-23**

Q2   Write down your ideas for how each of the characters could speak and move in these lines.

> CLAUDIO   Away! I will not have to do with you.
>
> LEONATO   Canst thou so daff me? Thou hast killed my child.
> If thou kill'st me, boy, thou shalt kill a man.
>
> ANTONIO   He shall kill two of us, and men indeed.
> But that's no matter, let him kill one first.
> Win me and wear me, let him answer me.
> Come follow me, boy. Come, sir boy, come, follow me.
> Sir boy, I'll whip you from your foining fence!
> Nay, as I am a gentleman, I will.
>
> LEONATO   Brother—
>
> ANTONIO   Content yourself. God knows I loved my niece,
> And she is dead, slandered to death by villains
>
> **Much Ado About Nothing, Act 5 Scene 1, lines 78-89**

Claudio and Leonato have been arguing over Hero's supposed death.

Q3   Write down any bits in the following extract where characters could emphasise their feelings through their movements, and suggest what those movements could be.

Subtle face movements? No problem.

> PROSPERO *(Aside)* I had forgot that foul conspiracy
> Of the beast Caliban and his confederates
> Against my life. The minute of their plot
> Is almost come. *(To the spirits)* Well done! Avoid — no more!
> *(the spirits depart)*
>
> FERDINAND   This is strange. Your father's in some passion
> That works him strongly.
>
> MIRANDA   Never till this day
> Saw I him touched with anger so distempered.
>
> **The Tempest, Act 4 Scene 1, lines 139-145**

Prospero has just remembered Caliban's plot against him and broken off the masque to celebrate Ferdinand and Miranda's engagement.

In this extract the movements are probably going to be quite subtle.
Think about facial expressions as well as big movements.

Revision Questions — Richard III

After you've answered parts a) to b) you can tackle the SAT question below. In the SAT you'll have to write about two separate bits from the play and they'll be quite a lot longer, but this is great practice.

> **Imagine you are directing this extract from *Richard III* for a class performance.**
> **Explain how the actors should play their parts.**

BUCKINGHAM   Welcome, sweet Prince, to London, to your chamber.
RICHARD   Welcome, dear cousin, my thoughts' sovereign.
The weary way hath made you melancholy.
PRINCE EDWARD   No, uncle, but our crosses on the way
Have made it tedious, wearisome, and heavy;
I want more uncles here to welcome me.

RICHARD   Sweet Prince, the untainted virtue of your years
Hath not yet dived into the world's deceit,
Nor more can you distinguish of a man
Than of his outward show, which — God He knows —
Seldom or never jumpeth with the heart:
Those uncles which you want were dangerous;
Your Grace attended to their sugared words,
But looked not on the poison of their hearts.
God keep you from them, and from such false friends!
PRINCE EDWARD   God keep me from false friends — but they were none.

RICHARD   My Lord, the Mayor of London comes to greet you.
Enter LORD MAYOR *with attendants.*
MAYOR   God bless your Grace with health and happy days!
PRINCE EDWARD   I thank you, good my lord, and thank you all.
I thought my mother and my brother York
Would long ere this have met us on the way.
Fie, what a slug is Hastings, that he comes not
To tell us whether they will come or no.
Enter HASTINGS
BUCKINGHAM   And in good time, here comes the sweating lord.

Richard III, Act 3 Scene 1, lines 1-24

The young Prince Edward has just been brought to the Tower by Richard and Buckingham. The Prince is unhappy that his relatives are not with him.

Q1 a)   I've stuck dotted lines onto the text to break it into chunks. Describe briefly what happens in each chunk.

b)   Write each of the characters' names at the top of a page. Under each heading answer these questions, covering one chunk of the extract at a time.

   i)   Who is the character talking to?
   ii)   How does the character feel? Back this up with a quote. ← *Say how they feel when they're speaking AND listening.*
   iii)   What movements can the actor use to show how the character feels?
   iv)   What tone of voice can the actor use to show how the character feels?
   v)   Should any words get extra emphasis from the actor's movements or tone of voice?

c)   Decide what order to cover your points in and write an answer to the question at the top of the page.   (18 marks)

You could write about one character at a time, or follow the order of the extract.

Revision Questions — Much Ado & The Tempest

Two more monster questions. Use part b) from page 84 to break them into bitesize bits.

Q1 **SAT-STYLE QUESTION** Imagine you are directing *Much Ado About Nothing*. Explain how the actor playing Leonato should show his feelings in these lines from the play. (18 marks)

Hero has fainted after Claudio's accusations.

BENEDICK   How doth the lady?
BEATRICE   Dead, I think. Help, uncle!
Hero! Why, Hero! Uncle! Signior Benedick! Friar!
LEONATO   O Fate! Take not away thy heavy hand.
Death is the fairest cover for her shame
That may be wished for.
BEATRICE   How now, cousin Hero!
FRIAR   Have comfort, lady.
LEONATO   Dost thou look up?
FRIAR   Yea, wherefore should she not?
LEONATO   Wherefore! Why, doth not every earthly thing
Cry shame upon her? Could she here deny
The story that is printed in her blood?
Do not live, Hero, do not ope thine eyes,
For did I think thou wouldst not quickly die,
Thought I thy spirits were stronger than thy shames,
Myself would, on the rearward of reproaches,
Strike at thy life. Grieved I, I had but one?

Chid I for that at frugal nature's frame?
O, one too much by thee! Why had I one?
Why ever wast thou lovely in my eyes?
Why had I not with charitable hand
Took up a beggar's issue at my gates,
Who smirched thus and mired with infamy,
I might have said "No part of it is mine —
This shame derives itself from unknown loins"?
But mine and mine I loved, and mine I praised
And mine that I was proud on, mine so much
That I myself was to myself not mine,
Valuing of her — why, she, O, she is fallen
Into a pit of ink, that the wide sea
Hath drops too few to wash her clean again,
And salt too little which may season give
To her foul-tainted flesh!

Much Ado About Nothing,
Act 4 Scene 1, lines 115-145

Q2 **SAT-STYLE QUESTION** Imagine you are directing this extract from *The Tempest*. Write instructions for the actors, concentrating on their movements and tone of voice. (18 marks)

Trinculo has just come across Caliban while looking for shelter.

TRINCULO   Warm, o' my troth! I do now let loose my opinion, hold it no longer — this is no fish, but an islander, that hath lately suffered by a thunderbolt. *(thunder)* Alas, the storm is come again! My best way is to creep under his gaberdine, there is no other shelter hereabout. Misery acquaints a man with strange bed-fellows. I will here shroud till the dregs of the storm be past.

Enter STEPHANO *singing, a bottle in his hand*

STEPHANO *(sings)* I shall no more to sea, to sea,
Here shall I die ashore —
This is a very scurvy tune to sing at a man's funeral.
Well, here's my comfort. *(drinks and sings)*
The master, the swabber, the boatswain, and I,
The gunner, and his mate,
Loved Mall, Meg, and Marian, and Margery,

But none of us cared for Kate,
For she had a tongue with a tang,
Would cry to a sailor 'Go hang!'
She loved not the savour of tar nor of pitch,
Yet a tailor might scratch her where'er she did itch.
Then to sea, boys, and let her go hang!
This is a scurvy tune too, but here's my comfort. *(drinks)*

CALIBAN   Do not torment me. O!

STEPHANO   What's the matter? Have we devils here? Do you put tricks upon's with savages and men of Ind? Ha! I have not scaped drowning to be afeard now of your four legs, for it hath been said, 'As proper a man as ever went on four legs cannot make him give ground,' and it shall be said so again, while Stephano breathes at nostrils.

CALIBAN   The spirit torments me. O!

The Tempest, **Act 2 Scene 2, lines 33-62**

Much Ado About a Shakespeare play...

Examiners always prefer it if you answer the exact question. If you don't they turn into slavering beasts. If they ask you to concentrate on movements, feelings or tone of voice, make sure you do.

Ideas, Themes and Issues in Richard III

The themes of a play are the big ideas that the play's about. If you get asked to write about themes in the SAT, you'll have to say how a certain bit of text relates to the main theme.

Q1   *Richard III is concerned with the importance of appearances.*
Answer all of the questions below about the themes in this extract.

> I, that am curtailed of this fair proportion,
> Cheated of feature by dissembling nature,
> Deformed, unfinished, sent before my time
> Into this breathing world, scarce half made up,
> And that so lamely and unfashionable
> That dogs bark at me as I halt by them —
> Why, I, in this weak piping time of peace,
> Have no delight to pass away the time,
> Unless to spy my shadow in the sun
> And descant on mine own deformity.
> And therefore, since I cannot prove a lover
> To entertain these fair well-spoken days,
> I am determined to prove a villain
> And hate the idle pleasures of these days.
>
> **Richard III, Act 1 Scene 1, lines 18-31**

dissembling = deceiving

descant = comment

a)   Write out all the parts of the speech that mention appearances.

b)   Write down what each one means.

c)   In your opinion, what does Richard think about appearances?

d)   What do you think Shakespeare is telling the audience about appearances in this speech?

Q2

SAT-STYLE QUESTION

What different ideas about good and evil does Shakespeare present in the speech (18 marks) below? Ask yourself questions like a)-d) above to help you plan your answer.

Enter the ghost of Prince Edward, son to Henry the Sixth
GHOST OF PRINCE EDWARD *(To Richard)*
Let me sit heavy on thy soul tomorrow.
Think how thou stab'st me in my prime of youth
At Tewkesbury; despair therefore, and die.
(To Richmond) Be cheerful, Richmond, for the
                                 wronged souls
Of butchered princes fight in thy behalf;
King Henry's issue, Richmond, comforts thee.
Enter ghost of Henry the Sixth
GHOST OF HENRY *(To Richard)*
When I was mortal, my anointed body
By thee was punched full of deadly holes.
Think of the Tower and me: despair and die!
Harry the Sixth bids thee despair, and die!
(To Richmond) Virtuous and holy, be thou conqueror:
Harry, that prophesied thou shouldst be King,

Doth comfort thee in thy sleep. Live and flourish!
Enter ghost of Clarence
GHOST OF CLARENCE *(To Richard)*
Let me sit heavy in thy soul tomorrow —
I, that was washed to death with fulsome wine,
Poor Clarence, by thy guile betrayed to death —
Tomorrow in the battle think of me,
And fall thy edgeless sword; despair and die.
(To Richmond) Thou offspring of the House of
                                   Lancaster,
The wronged heirs of York do pray for thee.
Good angels guard thy battle; live and flourish.

Richard III, Act 5 Scene 3, lines 119-139

Ideas, Themes and Issues in The Tempest

The Tempest is all about fate, justice and forgiveness.
You might get a SAT question asking you how the extract shows one of these main themes.

Q1   *One of the main themes of* The Tempest *is justice.*

> ARIEL   you three
> From Milan did supplant good Prospero,
> Exposed unto the sea, which hath requit it,
> Him, and his innocent child, for which foul deed
> The pow'rs, delaying, not forgetting, have
> Incensed the seas and shores, yea, all the creatures,
> Against your peace. Thee of thy son, Alonso,
> They have bereft, and do pronounce by me
> Ling'ring perdition, worse than any death
> Can be at once, shall step by step attend
> You and your ways, whose wraths to guard you from —
> Which here, in this most desolate isle, else falls
> Upon your heads — is nothing but heart's sorrow,
> And a clear life ensuing.
> ### *The Tempest*, Act 3 Scene 3, lines 69-82

requit = avenged

bereft = deprived, taken

perdition = loss, ruin

a) Write out all the parts of the speech that are about justice.

b) Write down what each one means in your own words.

c) Write down what you think Ariel is saying about justice.

d) What do you think Shakespeare thinks about justice?

Q2   **What different ideas about forgiveness does Shakespeare present in the speech**   (18 marks)
[SAT-STYLE QUESTION] **below? Ask yourself questions like a)-d) above to help you plan your answer.**

> ARIEL Him you termed, sir, 'the good old lord, Gonzalo'.
> His tears run down his beard, like winter's drops
> From eaves of reeds. Your charm so strongly works 'em
> That if you now beheld them your affections
> Would become tender.
> PROSPERO   Dost thou think so, spirit?
> ARIEL Mine would, sir, were I human.
> PROSPERO   And mine shall.
> Hast thou, which art but air, a touch, a feeling
> Of their afflictions, and shall not myself,
> One of their kind, that relish all as sharply,
> Passion as they, be kindlier moved than thou art?

> Though with their high wrongs I am struck to th'
>   quick,
> Yet with my nobler reason 'gainst my fury
> Do I take part. The rarer action is
> In virtue than in vengeance. They being penitent,
> The sole drift of my purpose doth extend
> Not a frown further. Go release them, Ariel.
> My charms I'll break, their senses I'll restore,
> And they shall be themselves.
> ### *The Tempest*, Act 5 Scene 1, lines 15-32

Ideas, Themes and Issues in Much Ado About Nothing

What have these things got in common: love, appearances, trickery and honour?
1) They're all themes of *Much Ado*, and 2) You might have to write about them in the SAT.

Q1   *This extract is about one of the big themes in* Much Ado About Nothing — *love.*

> BENEDICK   I pray thee now, tell me for which of my bad parts didst thou first fall in love with me?
>
> BEATRICE   For them all together, which maintained so politic a state of evil that they will not admit any good part to intermingle with them. But for which of my good parts did you first suffer love for me?
>
> BENEDICK   Suffer love! A good epithet! I do suffer love indeed, for I love thee against my will.
>
> BEATRICE   In spite of your heart, I think. Alas, poor heart! If you spite it for my sake, I will spite it for yours, for I will never love that which my friend hates.
>
> BENEDICK   Thou and I are too wise to woo peaceably.
>
> **Much Ado About Nothing**, Act 5 Scene 2, lines 56-65

a)   Write out any bits that talk about love.

b)   Write down what each one means.

c)   In your opinion, what does each of the characters think or feel about love?

d)   What do you think Shakespeare thinks about love?

Q2   **SAT-STYLE QUESTION**   What ideas about tricks does Shakespeare present in these speeches? Ask yourself questions like a)-d) above to help you plan your answer.

(18 marks)

> LEONATO   There was never counterfeit of passion came so near the life of passion as she discovers it.
>
> DON PEDRO   Why, what effects of passion shows she?
>
> CLAUDIO Bait the hook well — this fish will bite.
>
> LEONATO   What effects, my lord? She will sit you, you heard my daughter tell you how.
>
> CLAUDIO She did, indeed.
>
> DON PEDRO   How, how, pray you? You amaze me. I would have thought her spirit had been invincible against all assaults of affection.

> LEONATO   I would have sworn it had, my lord, especially against Benedick.
>
> BENEDICK I should think this is a gull but that the white-bearded fellow speaks it. Knavery cannot, sure, hide himself in such reverence.
>
> CLAUDIO He hath ta'en the infection. Hold it up.
>
> DON PEDRO   Hath she made her affection known to Benedick?
>
> LEONATO   No, and swears she never will. That's her torment.
>
> **Much Ado About Nothing**, Act 2 Scene 3, lines 104-124

Thertainly themes like the end to me...

Ouch, these questions are hard. For these ideas, themes and issues questions, work out the characters' ideas, then decide what overall message they add up to. Then have a nice lie down.

Answers

Reading Answers

Reading — The Basics

Page 2 Finding Facts

Q1

Description	Fact
Year HB Animation Studio was created	1998
Founded by...	Harold Black
Harold Black's current position	Managing Director
Total number of employees today	230

Q2 20 centimetres

Q3 wire frames (or armatures)

Q4 rod-and-joint structures

Q5 iii) 24

Q6 In order for the characters' movements to appear realistic on-screen.

Q7 The quality of its 3-D animation.

Page 3 Finding the Important Bits

Q1 a) Carrie darted round the corner into a dingy side street full of discarded wooden crates.

b) ...followed by Ben, who stopped and bent over, panting.

He felt like he'd been out of breath ever since...

c) ...ever since they'd left the Pirate Academy.

d) ...the leering, cruel face of Captain Hack.

e) ...must walk the plank.

f) ...any student failing to hand in homework...

g) Ben dashed forward with a yell, and managed to slip between Captain Hack's legs.

h) Ben ripped a thin plank of wood from a nearby crate.

Q2 Suddenly they were aware of a shadow looming over them.

Q3 She's about to use it as a sword against Captain Hack. The part of the text is: "Then she remembered her sword-fighting lessons, and crouched with the plank in her hand, ready to defend herself against her pirate tutor."

Page 4 Backing Up Points

Q1 Hanif strongly dislikes the rabbits and wants to get rid of them.

Q2 iii) Hanif wants to get rid of the rabbits. He calls them 'stinking', which shows that he doesn't like them.

Q3 i) Hanif has a strong opinion about the rabbits.

Q4 Milla is nervous.

Q5 Milla glanced around the street nervously

Q6 ii) Milla seems to be worried that someone will see her dumping the envelope into the bin.

Q7 Miles says that he'll be fine, but the fact that there is 'a hint of a tear in his eye' shows that he's not fine at all, and he's just being brave about his feelings.

Page 5 Summarising

Q1 The king, Felix, the king's courtier, Prime Minister Katan, two attendants (and the captured knights and the dragon for extra points!)

Q2 The king and Felix

Q3 The king remembers when his father was king, and knights were **easier** to control. **He starts to think about his childhood when he played with toys in the garden.** Then he decides that something must be done about the knights.

Q4 ii) He seems angry with Felix, but is easily distracted by memories of his childhood.

Q5 The king accuses Felix of failing to stop the knights from escaping. He tells Prime Minister Katan to tie Felix up, take him to Vertis Ledge, and leave him to the dragons.

Q6 The king is angry because all of his captured knights have escaped. He reminisces about when his father was king and his own childhood. He blames Felix for allowing the knights to escape. He instructs the Prime Minister to tie Felix up and leave him to the dragons on Vertis Ledge. As Felix is taken away, he threatens the king.

Page 6 Different Types of Text

Q1 Epilepsy — The Facts — A
Using your T-300 — D
Waiting — B
A man alone — C

Q2 A and D

Q3 B and C

Q4 Poem — B
Story — C
Manual — D
Magazine article — A

Q5 a) D

b) B

c) A

d) C

Reading — Working Things Out

Page 7 Working Out What's Going On

Q1

Event	Order in extract
Looks for tickets	2
Puts milk bottles outside	5
Wakes up	1
Has an accident in the kitchen	3
Puts front doors keys with tickets	4

Q2 • without them she *definitely* wouldn't be going on holiday today.

Q3 • before sacrificing two of the dishes to the floor in a flurry of ceramic and congealed Chinese takeaway.

Q4 ii) Mrs Hanrahan knocked over two dirty dishes, and they smashed on the floor.

Q5 The front door locks behind her.

Q6 *Any sensible answer is OK, e.g.:*
Mrs Hanrahan won't be able to get back into the house because the front door has locked and she left the keys inside. She won't be able to get the tickets, so she won't be able to go on holiday.

Reading Answers

Page 8 Working Out What's Going On

Q1 Using automatic cameras rather than manual cameras, and not developing the films yourself.

Q2 Film speed — "'Slow' films are suitable for normal lighting, whereas you'll need to use a faster ISO 400 film to take pictures on gloomy days (or as fast as ISO 1000 if it's night-time)."

Q3 ISO 100, because the text says that ISO 400 is fast and ISO 1000 is even faster.

Q4 The next issue of the magazine will feature an article about developing pictures in a darkroom.

Q5

Camera setting	Set to...	Reason
Film speed	ISO 400	Bright light
Aperture setting	Narrow	Bright light
Shutter speed	Short	Detailed action shots

Q6

Camera setting	Set to...	Reason
Film speed	ISO 1000	In the dark
Aperture setting	Wide	In the dark
Shutter speed	Long	Blurry pictures

Q7
- The writer says that automatic cameras are easier because you just have to 'point, press, and get someone else to do the dirty work'.
- You have to think about the type of film to use.
- You have to work out aperture settings.
- You have to think about shutter speed.
- You usually have to do the focusing yourself.
- You may have to develop the pictures yourself in a darkroom.

This question is like the kind of thing you get in the SAT. If you mention any 5 of the things above, you should get 5 marks.

Page 9 Working Out How Characters Feel

Q1
- towards Camelot and the King he had wished never to see again

Q2 i) Lancelot wishes he was free to go where he wanted and didn't have to walk any more.

Q3
- trudge grimly
- hack his way wearily

Q4
- if only to be finally at peace
Lancelot is so tired that even being dead sounds pleasant because then he could rest.

Q5
- Had to cut through dense foliage — Tired and frustrated
- Waded through rivers and walked in wet clothes — Uncomfortable
- Killed many other knights — Sad because he respected them

Q6 Points that could be made:
- Lancelot would be mentally and physically exhausted
- He would be moving very slowly by then
- He would be uncomfortable
- He wouldn't want to see the King
- He would be upset at having killed other knights

Reading — The Way It's Written

Page 10 Descriptions

Q1

Thing being described	How it's described
The whole city	Peaceful
The light from the lamp	Flickering
The doorway	Narrow
The dogs guarding the doorway	Snarling
The sheet of paper	Faded and yellow
Inspector Graham's hand	Trembling
The inside of the room	Dim

Q2
- flickering lamplight
- snarling dogs
- trembling hand
- dim inside of the room

Q3
- a small stone carving of a man crouching as if about to pounce at the Inspector

Q4 iii) The statue is described as if it is alive — this effect is called personification.

Q5
- The river flowed gently past the houses as if it didn't want to wake up the slumbering inhabitants

Q6
- The writer builds up suspense by describing the quiet city.
- Inspector Graham expects trouble at any moment
- Inspector Graham is nervous — his hand trembles
- The night before Graham had come across snarling dogs guarding the doorway
- The door creaks open, which sounds scary
- The lamplight flickers and the room is very dim
- The stone carving is described as if it is alive and about to attack the Inspector

This question is like the kind you'll get in the SAT. Any 5 of the things above would get you 5 marks.

Page 11 Descriptions of Characters

Q1 ii) Sarah seems to feel sorry for David and tries to keep him happy.

Q2
- surveyed him with a slightly pitying look
- Sarah tried to keep smiling, but failed

Q3 David — short-tempered, stressed
Sarah — sympathetic, tolerant
Denise — arrogant, stunning

Reading Answers

Q4   David — short-tempered:
- He wheeled around abruptly
- He grabbed Sarah by the lapels of her smart jacket
- "And *where* is our leading lady?" demanded David

David — stressed:
- asked David in a shaky voice
- he started to pull at the few tufts of greying hair left on his head
- his eyes darting from side to side as if following the path of a wasp

Sarah — sympathetic, tolerant
- surveyed him with a slightly pitying look
- Sarah tried to keep smiling, but failed

Denise — arrogant:
- "Your ravishing, immensely talented leading lady has just entered the building,"
- A figure sauntered casually into the light
- She tossed back her mane of honey-coloured hair
- fixed David with a commanding gaze

Denise — stunning:
- said a silky voice
- She tossed back her mane of honey-coloured hair
- Denise continued in a steady, alluring tone

Q5
- The fact that Denise tosses her hair makes her sound confident and arrogant
- Denise's hair is described as a mane, which makes her sound like a lion, which is a very impressive, aggressive and proud animal
- Denise's hair is described as honey-coloured, which makes it sound very pretty but maybe a bit sickly too

Q6   The fact that Denise saunters into the room makes her sound very confident and arrogant

Q7
- David is tired and nervous, which contrasts with Sarah, who is described as 'fresh-faced'
- David is very nervous, which contrasts with Denise, who saunters into the room and has a 'commanding gaze'
- Sarah tries to be kind to David, which contrasts with Denise, who seems to look down at David

This question is like the kind you'll get in the SAT. If you mentioned the last 3 points, backed up with your answers to Q3 and Q4, you'd get 5 marks.

Page 12 Similes and Metaphors

Q1 a) neither

b) simile

c) metaphor

Q2 ii) The shouting audience sounded noisy and tuneless, like wolf howls.

Q3   simile

Q4

Thing being described	Description the writer uses	Simile or metaphor	What this means
Leo Ryder	he was a monster	metaphor	he was angry and impressive
Richie Z playing guitar	possessed by the ghost of Jimi Hendrix	metaphor	he played as well as Jimi Hendrix
Jay Bryson beating the drums	as if they were fires to be put out	simile	he looked panicked
	he managed to keep time as faithfully as an honest referee	simile	he kept time very well

Page 13 Mood

Q1   A — tense
B — sad
C — happy

Q2   No. She watches her friends open their envelopes first, and then opens hers very slowly:
- Her fingers tugged gently at the envelope

Q3   The word 'weep' makes it sound as if the ceilings are crying and upset, just like the family after the dog died

Q4   It shows that Daniel is happy, because it makes him sound like an animal without any worries

Q5 i) They slow the pace down before Rachel opens the envelope, which builds up suspense.

Q6   B — the phrase 'long, pale faces' sounds very sad

Q7   It shows that the family are sad about the dog — they don't speak very much or make eye contact. The phrase makes the whole text seem very sad.

Pages 14/15 Long Language Question

Q1
- rounded bodies
- new and ghastly looking creatures
- in shape somewhat resembling an octopus
- with huge and very long and flexible tentacles
- The skin had a glistening texture, unpleasant to see, like shiny leather
- They were the size of a fair-sized swine
- the tentacles seemed to be many feet in length

Q2

Any picture that looks a bit like this is fine.

Q3   Adjectives:
i) wave-worn
ii) horrible
iii) ghastly
v) flexible
vi) glistening
ix) revolting

Adverbs:
iv) copiously
vii) flatly
viii) intensely
x) slowly

Q4 ii) The skin had a glistening texture, unpleasant to see, like shiny leather.

Q5
- it does not appear that Mr Fison was afraid, or that he realised that he was in any danger
- he was horrified, of course, and intensely excited and indignant

Q6
- large intelligent eyes
- gave the creatures a grotesque suggestion of a face
- their eyes regarded him with evil interest
- making a soft purring sound to each other

Q7
- The rounded bodies fell apart
- slowly uncoiling their tentacles
- creeping at first deliberately

Reading Answers

Q8 iii) Very slowly — Builds up suspense

Q9 • The writer describes the creatures as 'ghastly looking'
• The writer uses the simile that the creatures' skin had a 'glistening texture, unpleasant to see, like shiny leather', which makes them sound very ugly.
• The creatures move slowly, which builds up suspense and makes the creatures seem more menacing.
• The writer says that Mr Fison is 'horrified' at seeing the creatures.
• The writer uses personification in phrases like 'their eyes regarded him with evil interest' to show that the creatures are intelligent, which makes them seem more horrific.
This question is very like the kind you'll get in the SAT. If you make 5 points similar to the ones above, you should get 10 marks.

Page 16 Layout

Q1 A diary or journal — each entry is dated, and the language is abbreviated and informal.

Q2 To show when things happened, and to point out the start of each entry.

Q3 ii) To make the article feel like a conversation between the writer and the reader.

Q4 To make the text easier to follow, and to make it easy to refer back to points quickly.

Q5 Extra tips and explanations of the information in the list.

Q6 They link each tip to the correct numbered point.

Page 17 Structure

Q1 • It draws the reader in because it points out that the reader won't have heard of Alexis Bright, but soon he will be very famous.
• The reader will want to know why Alexis Bright will become famous.

Q2 The writer explains what kind of book 'A Tale of Two Celebrities' is, and what happens in the book.

Q3 • The first paragraph introduces Alexis Bright and the second paragraph tells you what the review is about.
• After reading the first paragraph, the reader will want to know what Alexis Bright has done that will make him famous.

Q4 • The third paragraph explains why some people will like the book, and why it will be a big seller
• The fourth paragraph explains why some people won't like the book

Q5 To contrast the two different opinions that people will have about the book.

Q6 i) The last sentence refers back to the introduction and sums up the main point of the review.

Q7 *If you mention your answers to questions 1, 3, 5 and 6 you'll get your 10 marks.*

Reading — The Writer's Viewpoint

Page 18 Persuading the Reader

Q1 To make the reader buy Bonza Biscuits

Q2 • luxury biscuit treat
• Not only are they tasty, they're great value too
• the most satisfying chocolate biscuits you'll ever have

Q3

Body part	Description
legs	like tree trunks
forehead	damp
hands	pudgy and clay-like
eyes	narrow and squinting
nose	peeling

Q4 iii) Mr Blister is a really ugly and unpleasant man

Q5 • The writer does not want the reader to like Mr Blister.
• He is described as very ugly (with 'peeling nose' and 'damp forehead'), which makes him sound unpleasant to look at.
• Also, the writer says that Mr Blister thinks of people as 'idiots' that 'made him feel ill', which makes him sound very mean too.
If you mention the three points above (but you could use different examples to back them up) then you'll get your 3 marks.

Page 19 Changes in the Writer's Opinion

Q1 i) My parents saw it as an educational experience

Q2 The writer goes backstage at Jackson's Travelling Circus, and doesn't like what she sees

Q3 The third paragraph

Q4 Unfortunately, the reality of the circus was far less exotic than I had previously believed

Q5 The sight of the elephants pacing sadly up and down brought tears to my eyes

Q6 • The answer is wrong because the writer used to love circuses, but now she thinks they're a bit cruel. The question mark in the title wouldn't back up that answer anyway.
• A better answer would be: The writer added a question mark to the title 'All The Fun of the Fair?' to show that she used to believe that circuses were great, but now she's not so sure.

Q7 *If you mention your answers to questions 1-6 you'll get your 5 marks.*

Page 20 The Effect on the Reader

Q1 The narrator is a criminal. He and his gang have been trying to rob a safe, and the criminal thinks that his partners have all been captured.

Q2 • Wouldn't you?

Q3 ii) It sounds as if the character is talking to you and it involves you in the decision.

Q4 iii) The writer wants to make the reader feel like they're actually taking part in the story.

Q5 • you and I know that there would have been no point
• surely you don't think I was unreasonable

Reading Answers

Q6
- The writer asks the reader to 'imagine the situation', which encourages them to become involved in the story.
- The writer uses rhetorical questions to make the reader feel as if they're involved in the main character's decisions.
- The main character addresses the reader directly in phrases like 'you and I know', which makes the reader feel that they know the main character.

If you mention any three points like the ones above then you'll get 5 marks.

Reading — Comparing Texts

Page 21/22/23 Comparing Texts

Q1 *The Macaque Monkeys of Japan* — Diary
I, Monkey — Story
Monkey Behaviour — Magazine article

Q2
- they're excited and buzzing around like annoying flies

Q3
- they're excited and buzzing around like annoying flies
- the cheek of it!
- maybe have a chat about the weather

Q4
- It worked!

Many phrases contain abbreviated language too, such as:
- Macaque monkeys currently living in the centre of the island

Q5
- To make the text easier to follow
- To divide the text up into days because it is a diary

Q6 i) Macaque monkeys currently living in the centre of the island

Q7 ii) The monkey is more intelligent than the scientists realise. The monkey tells the story from his point of view, which shows the scientists are wrong.

Q8 i) The writer thinks that humans are not ruled by instinct, but that all animals and insects are.

Q9 ii) All three texts are about whether the behaviour of monkeys is purely instinctive.

Q10

Name of extract	The Macaque Monkeys of Japan	I, Monkey	Monkey Behaviour
Is the extract fiction or non-fiction?	non-fiction	fiction	non-fiction
Is descriptive language used?	No	Yes	No
Is the language formal or informal?	Informal	Informal	Formal
Is there a first-person narrator?	Yes	Yes	No
Does the writer use facts to back up their points?	Yes	No	Yes
Does the writer think that animals are ruled by instinct?	No	No	Yes

Q11
- *The Macaque Monkeys of Japan* is broken up into the days that things are happening. This makes the text easy to follow and it also shows where each new day begins.
- *The Macaque Monkeys of Japan* was written one day at a time, so the structure just follows the order that things happened.
- *I, Monkey* is laid out in long paragraphs.
- *I, Monkey* starts with the monkey explaining what has happened, and ends with him saying that he plans to escape.

If you mention any three of the points above, you'll get 3 marks.

Q12
- *I, Monkey* uses informal language.
- *I, Monkey* uses humour in phrases like 'the cheek of it!'
- *Monkey Behaviour* uses formal language.
- There is no humour in *Monkey Behaviour*.

If you mention any three of the points above, you'll get 3 marks.

Q13
- The writer of *The Macaque Monkeys of Japan* is trying to prove that the behaviour patterns of monkeys can change.
- By the end of the *The Macaque Monkeys of Japan* the writer feels he has proved that monkeys are not ruled by instinct.
- The writer of *Monkey Behaviour* thinks that all animals and insects are purely ruled by instinct.
- The writer of *Monkey Behaviour* believes that only humans are not purely ruled by instinct.

If you mention any three of the points above, you'll get 3 marks.

Reading — Revision Questions

Page 24/25 Answers Without Prompts

Q1 Wilde writes that 'a sharp pang of pain struck like a knife across him', and this **simile** shows that Dorian feels physically hurt when he realises that he will grow old. Later, Dorian **panics** when Wilde writes that 'he felt as if a hand of ice had been laid upon his heart'.

Q2
- How does Hallward feel about his painting?
- How does Lord Henry react to seeing the painting?
- What do the characters say to Dorian before and after seeing the painting?

Q3
- The first two prompts ask how Lord Henry and Hallward feel about each other, but the question asks about how they feel about **Dorian**.
- The third prompt asks about what Dorian thinks about the painting, but the question asks about how **Lord Henry** and **Basil Hallward** act.

Q4
- How does the language make the reader feel about old age?
- Which phrases describe Dorian's body when he is old?
- Does Oscar Wilde use similes and metaphors in the extract?

Q5 *Any reasonable set of three prompts, for example:*
- How does Dorian feel about old age at the beginning of the extract?
- What happens to change Dorian's opinion of old age?
- How does Dorian feel about old age at the end of the extract?

Reading Answers

Q6 i) Dorian isn't really aware of his beauty and doesn't believe the nice things that people say.

Q7
• Basil Hallward's compliments had seemed to him to be merely the charming exaggerations of friendship.
• He had listened to them, laughed at them, forgotten them.
• They had not influenced his nature.
• The sense of his own beauty came on him like a revelation.

Q8 He sees Hallward's painting of himself.

Q9 ii) Dorian realises that he is as beautiful as people have been telling him.

Q10
• The sense of his own beauty came on him like a revelation.

Q11 Dorian imagines when his face is 'wrinkled and wizen' and he feels so horrified that the thought hurts 'like a **knife** across him'. He imagines when 'the scarlet would pass away from his lips', which shows that he thinks that he will become **ugly**.

Q12 Dorian wishes that the portrait could grow old instead of him, so that he can always stay the same age.

Q13 *Any three reasonable prompts, for example:*
• How does Dorian feel about himself at the start of the extract?
• What happens to make Dorian change his opinion of himself?
• How does Dorian feel about his appearance afterwards?
• How does Dorian feel about growing old?
• What does Dorian wish for at the end of the extract?

Q14
• At the beginning of the extract Dorian doesn't believe people when they say that he is beautiful.
• Dorian's opinion of himself changes as soon as he sees the portrait of himself.
• When Dorian sees the portrait, he realises that he is as beautiful as people have said.
• Dorian imagines when he is old, and hates the idea.
• At the end of the extract Dorian wishes that he will never grow old.
This question is very like the kind you might get in the SAT. If you mention the five points above, you'll get 5 marks.

Page 26/27 Proper SAT Reading Questions

Q1 Uruguay

Q2

Description of fact	Number
Year of first World Cup final	1930
Largest stadium audience	200,000
Year Football Association was created	1963
Total viewing figures of 1998 World Cup	33.4 billion
Year Charles Miller took football to Brazil	1894
Number of teams playing in first World Cup Final	13
Year World Cup match sparked a war	1969

Q3 China — 5000 years ago

Q4 El Salvador and Honduras

Q5 Jules Rimet

Q6 Paris

Q7
• It's a joke
• The history actually goes back a very long time — about 5000 years

Q8
• The simile makes the fans sound crazy
• The fans sound like a big pack of fierce animals

Q9
• The metaphor makes the football games sound like battles
• It makes it sound as if there are no rules and people might get hurt

Q10
• To show that there are three separate ideas about why football is popular
• To make it easy to follow the text and to refer back to the points

Q11
• To make the reader feel like it's a conversation between themselves and the writer
• To show what each paragraph is about, and the question that each paragraph addresses

Q12
• It doesn't explain that the text is about the World Cup until the end of the first paragraph, which encourages the reader to keep reading to find out what's going on
• The first paragraph starts by putting the reader in the middle of the action, which is quite exciting
• The writer uses a simile ('snarling like hyenas') to make the description exciting
• The writer uses humour in the phrase 'this is not a scene from *Braveheart*', which might entertain the reader
Any three of the points above will get you 3 marks.

Q13

Subsection	Summary
Introduction	Tells you what the article is about and the first World Cup
'Where did football come from?'	The origins of football and how the rules were formed
'Is it really the beautiful game?'	The ways that football has been responsible for bad things
'What's so great about football?'	The popularity of football, and reasons why it is popular
'Who are the biggest football fans?'	The most football-mad fans and the 2002 World Cup

Q14 *Any reasonable summary, for example:*
The article explains the history of football and the World Cup. It describes some good and bad things that football has caused. It tries to explain why it is so popular and finishes by discussing the 2002 World Cup.

Q15
• it hasn't all been good
• these idiots continue to spoil the game for many other people

Q16
• He brought two footballs to Brazil
• He introduced football to Brazil

Q17
• The 'shrill blast' is the referee's whistle
• The ''thunk' of leather against leather' is the sound of a football being kicked by footballers wearing boots

Q18
• The rules are simple
• It doesn't take much organising to start a game
• There are often very dramatic incidents in the games

Q19 *Any reasonable answer, for example:*
• The ending talks about something that the reader will know about - i.e. the 2002 World Cup
• The writer talks about himself, saying that he also got caught up in the excitement - this makes the ending more personal
• The article ends with a bit of humour, when the writer says that he still doesn't understand the offside rule

Reading Answers

Q20 *Any reasonable answer, for example:*
- The writer thinks that football is exciting (he compares a match to a scene from *Braveheart* in the first paragraph)
- The writer knows that football is popular - he says it's the 'game we know and love'
- The writer doesn't like people spoiling football - he calls football hooligans 'idiots'
- He says that he got caught up in the national excitement surrounding the 2002 World Cup
- He doesn't really understand football completely - he says he doesn't understand the offside rule

Each of the points above will get you one mark, up to a maximum of 5 marks.

Q21
- The writer uses a popular reference in the phrase 'this is not a scene from *Braveheart*' in the first paragraph, which will entertain the reader
- The writer says that the World Cup is more serious than *Braveheart* in the first paragraph, which makes it sound a lot more important than it really is
- The writer says that 'The history of football goes back ever so slightly further than 1930', which is funny because football is about 5000 years old - this makes the reader feel that the article isn't just about dry facts and figures
- The writer compares Medieval football to a battlefield, which is funny because it shows the reader how different football used to be
- The article ends with humour, when the writer says that he still doesn't understand the offside rule - this makes the reader laugh at the end of the article and shows that the article was supposed to be fun

Each of the points above will get you one mark, up to a maximum of 5 marks.

Q22 *Any reasonable answers, for example:*
- The writer shows that football can be scary in the first paragraph, when he compares football fans to snarling hyenas
- The writer shows that the history of football hasn't been all nice, such as the Italians using a head as a ball
- The writer implies that Charles Miller introducing football to Brazil was a good thing, because now Brazil is 'the home of the most beautifully-played football in the world'
- The writer says that football hooligans 'spoil the game', and he calls them 'idiots'
- The writer says that even he got caught up in the national excitement, so he seems to believe that it's good that everyone gets excited about the same thing

Any five points like the ones above will get you 5 marks.

Writing Answers

Writing — Grammar, Vocabulary and Spelling

Page 28 Sentences, Phrases and Clauses

Q1 a) no full stop

b) no verb

c) no full stop

d) no verb

e) no subject, e.g. "he"

f) no capital letter at the beginning, no full stop

g) no verb

h) no subject, e.g. "he"

i) no verb

Q2 a) phrase

b) clause

c) main clause

d) clause

e) phrase

f) main clause

g) phrase

h) main clause

i) phrase

Q3 a) Before the start of term, I'll have to cram in lots of fun.

b) In the Atlantic ocean, you can see fish swimming.

c) In his best Western movies, Gary Cooper's acting was impressive.

d) Without a bit of mustard, this recipe tastes disgusting.

e) Without a doubt, porridge is better than gruel.

f) Very well then, I'll fight you for it.

g) In a desperate attempt at humour, Kim threw the egg against the wall.

h) Up in the attic, my brother tried to poison a rat.

Page 29 Commas, Semicolons and Colons

Q1 a) Walking beside the miniature poodle, Harley felt very tall indeed.

b) Helen pitied the spider in the sink, which was about to die.

c) Scurrying out of the way of the headmistress, Dana looked a bit sheepish.

d) He walked and talked, half an hour afterwards his head was cut off.

Q2 a) After the storm was over, my sister returned to the ranch.

b) Despite everything, I still had a soft spot for her.

c) He marched away from the station, without a single look back.

d) Way back, many centuries ago, not long after the Bible began, Jacob lived in the land of Canaan, a fine example of a family man.

e) Although the weather was hot, Abigail decided to wear a big jumper and corduroy jeans.

Q3 a) I'll tell you how I managed it: I walked up to him and asked him.

b) All I want from my hamster is: companionship, devotion and a small but tasty meal.

c) As my grandmother says: "Don't fight with your Grandad

or I'll get you."

d) You should bring the following things: an inflatable dinghy, a life jacket and a foghorn.

e) Pigeons have been known to communicate as follows: "eeuak, eak, ouawk, ek-ek, ooch."

Q4 a) The star required: a trailer with a jacuzzi; three servants including a manicurist; a separate dog kennel and Scottish salmon sandwiches without crusts.

b) The footballer had it all: a strong left foot; a good eye for the ball; a lightning pace and nerves of steel.

c) He walked into the room; he had never been inside before.

d) Jim had made a huge pile; he owned a large percentage of the Nile.

Page 30 Apostrophes

Q1 a) Our son might not be perfect, but theirs is atrocious.

b) There's a small cat which lives in our barn.

c) It's sunny outside, why stay indoors?

d) The driver wanted the car repaired because its gearbox was making funny noises.

e) I really like the theatre; there's a good one in my home town.

f) It's is used correctly.

g) "It's a Wonderful Life" is a film with Jimmy Stewart. It's shown every Christmas.

Q2 a) The ostriches' beaks were all shiny.

b) My brother Alex's band are playing in the pub on Saturday.

c) She gave him her mum's favourite handkerchief, realising too late that it was covered in snot.

d) The children's section of the menu was uninspiring.

e) Elmer McCurdy's body was used as a fairground attraction for seventy years before people realised it was human and gave him a proper burial.

f) Marcus's piano was six feet tall; he couldn't reach the pedals.

Q3 a) I don't want to trouble you, but your Alsatian is in my garage.

b) The boxer won't fight without his lucky rabbit's foot.

c) Don't you think it's strange how television stars get thinner every year?

d) It's the best piece of music I've ever heard.

e) It isn't that unusual for people to have two part-time jobs.

f) I can't go to the gym. I won't go to the gym. I don't want to go to the gym.

Page 31 Speech, Question and Exclamation Marks

Q1 a) When asked if he was a communist, Ring Lardner Jr. replied, "I could tell you but I would hate myself in the morning."

c) Bette Davis said the famous line, "Fasten your seat belts, it's going to be a bumpy night," in the film 'All About Eve'.

d) When Tony Blair got into power, he kept saying, "Education, education, education."
b) and e) don't need speech marks.

Writing Answers

Q2 Jake burst through the door of the garage shop.

"Freeze!" he shouted. He was scared; he could feel the sweat rolling down his forehead and flooding his eyes. He moved towards the cashier, holding the bag out in one hand, grasping his fake gun in the other.

"Oh my life!" said the cashier, "Jake Smithson, what are you doing?" Jake stopped in his tracks. He had been told that a pair of tights over the head would render any human being unrecognisable. Maybe 15 denier wasn't enough.

"I'm not Jake Smithson," he said, backing away.

"Yes you are, I used to serve you lunch at St Hilda's Primary School. Fancy that! What are you getting up to these days?" she said. Quietly, she pressed the police alarm under the counter.

Q3 a) "I'm hard to get," said Slim, "all you have to do is ask."

b) "My name is Maximus Decimus Meridus," said the stranger, "and I will have my vengeance in this life or the next."

c) "I think I'm falling in love with her," said Fritz.
"Oh, I am sorry," said Brian.
"So am I," said Fritz.

d) "She was awfully decent about that cheese," said Caldicott.
"But I see she didn't leave much of the pickles," said Charters.

e) "I demand that you pay me one million dollars," said Dr Evil.

f) "You say you're alone but your table's set for four," said the policeman.
"That's nothing," the man replied, "my alarm clock's set for eight."

Page 32 Writing Interesting Sentences

Q1 a) Jim ran to the station because he needed to catch the last train.

b) I am prepared to wait until the governor decides what will happen.

c) Sergei Bubka thinks he is the best pole-vaulter in the world but I am better.

d) I was about to go shopping when the letter landed on the mat.

e) My ceramic frog collection is terrific and it's worth a lot of money too.

Q2 a) Isabel had only got one ticket. She didn't want to give it away.

b) Pancakes with sugar and lemon are good. Jam filling is also nice.

c) Daria flew over the wall. She landed in a heap at the bottom of the ditch.

d) St Malo is really hot in the summer. You can go swimming in the sea.

e) Una was going to miss the plane. Perhaps she could grab a lift on the boy's skateboard.

Q3 a) Don't we all know that paint dries slowly?

b) Surely we all know that the governor will be back next year?

c) Surely you're not saying that Muriel's lying?

d) Cybil didn't know where to look; hadn't that man left five days ago?

Q4 *e.g.*
Rita Hayworth was born in 1918 in America. Her family were Spanish and her original name was Margarita Cansino. From the age of 13 she danced in a stage act with her father. She spent a lot of time practising her dancing, which meant she missed out on most of her education. In the late 1930s, she started to get small roles in films. However, the American film industry was xenophobic and didn't like the fact that she looked Spanish. Her appearance was therefore changed in the following ways: her black hair was dyed red and her hairline was made higher by electrolysis. In addition to this, her Spanish-sounding name was changed to Rita Hayworth.

Page 33 Writing Interesting Sentences

Q1 a) Even though it was raining, I dashed to the supermarket.

b) It didn't matter if the police caught me any more; I had to stop running.

c) In the autumn, I will go on a fantastic holiday to Iceland.

d) "Please go away," I said.

e) Suddenly worried, I opened the satchel.

Q2 *e.g.*
a) drove

b) hurried

c) flew

d) trudged

e) ambled

Q3 a) he

b) it

c) They

d) she, him

e) She, him

Q4 *Possible answer:*
Franz Fanon was born in the French colony of Martinique. He trained as a psychologist in France. He encountered racism there. He then decided to move to Algeria, which was a French colony. During his time there, he worked at a hospital.
Franz Fanon supported the Algerian revolution against French colonial rule which started in 1954. It was very bitter and violent. In his role as a psychologist, Franz Fanon treated both French soldiers who had tortured Algerian revolutionaries, and the victims of torture. He wrote a book about the revolution, called 'A Dying Colonialism'. It is very good.

Page 34 Writing Interesting Sentences

Q1 a) active

i) passive

b) passive

ii) active

c) active

iii) passive

d) passive

iv) active

Q2 a) Be quiet in the museum.

   b) Don't smoke in the flammable wigwam.

   c) Try eating the frosted peas.

   d) Go down to the dock of the bay.

Q3

What Leo said to John in the pub last night	How likely is it that Leo will buy the beer?
"I should buy some of your homemade beer."	he feels he ought to buy it, but it isn't definite that he will
"I might buy some of your homemade beer."	it's possible he will buy the beer
"If I was richer, I would buy your homemade beer."	he won't buy the beer
"I will buy some of your homemade beer"	he'll definitely buy the beer
"I can buy your homemade beer."	he is able to buy it, but it isn't definite that he will

Page 35 Vocabulary

Q1 *Possible answers (the nouns have been underlined):*

   a) The cautious <u>boy</u> was scared that the ravenous <u>dog</u> would attack him.

   b) Long-distance <u>swimming</u> is good <u>exercise</u>.

   c) Poor <u>Orpheus</u> knew that he shouldn't look, but the overwhelming <u>temptation</u> to see his beloved <u>wife</u> was too much.

   d) A gigantic <u>wave</u> came towards the little <u>shore</u> and drenched the unsuspecting <u>sunbathers</u>.

   e) In the play <u>park</u> near my beautiful <u>house</u> there is an ancient <u>oak tree</u>.

   f) I didn't know until that terrible <u>moment</u> how I would cope in such a challenging <u>situation</u>.

   g) It was three long <u>days</u> before they realised that the intrepid <u>hamster</u> had escaped.

   h) "It is a well-known <u>fact</u> that gorgeous <u>Robert Mitchum</u> is a brilliant <u>actor</u>," said my <u>mum</u>.

Q2 a) Maria turned to Emma and whispered, "I think we should be quiet, no one else is talking in here."

   b) Maria turned to Emma and bellowed, "Get out of my sight, you ungrateful, horrible woman."

   c) Maria turned to Emma and warbled, "The hills are alive with the sound of music."

   d) Maria turned to Emma and groaned, "Not another gas bill."

   e) Maria turned to Emma and griped, "All the other waitresses get better tips than me."

Q3 *Possible answers (the verbs have been underlined):*

   a) Jane warmly <u>welcomed</u> the professor.

   b) The captain <u>shouted</u> menacingly at his daughter.

   c) I <u>walked</u> slowly down to the riverbank.

   d) The cat <u>eyed</u> the salmon hungrily.

   e) "Surely not the Maltese Falcon!" said Sam excitedly.

   f) The robber was <u>caught</u> dramatically in the street.

   g) The mastermind <u>paced</u> thoughtfully up and down the dank room.

Page 36 Vocabulary

Q1 *Possible answer:*

	The girl was <u>nice</u>.	The play was <u>interesting</u>.	The results were <u>bad</u>.	She's <u>good</u> at the piano.	The sea captain was <u>old</u>.
informal word	friendly	watchable	awful	fantastic	ancient
formal word	pleasant	engrossing	unfortunate	talented	elderly

Q2 *Possible answers:*

   a) invaded, really annoying, for starters, squawk, can't hear yourself think, let alone, plus, poo

   b) The pigeons, which started living in the church steeple two months ago, are causing disruption. For example, they make a lot of noise, distracting people and drowning out the sound of the choir. Also, we have to put up with bird excrement in the choir stalls. It really is too much to bear.

Q3 Adjectives: blue, quiet, old, quiet, awful
Adverbs: slowly, very much, slowly, quickly
Possible answer (adjectives and adverbs have been underlined):

Paul walked <u>timidly</u> down to the dock. The <u>mysterious</u> boat was still there, docked at the end of the <u>gloomy</u> jetty. He hoped <u>feverishly</u> that the man had gone. There was a storm gathering <u>rapidly</u> overhead. He realised <u>suddenly</u> that it had grown dark. He took off his shoes and climbed onto the deck. There was the <u>familiar</u> door, with the scorch marks from the fire still there. From beyond the door he heard a <u>crackling</u> voice:
"Come in my child. You are welcome here."
Paul was struck by a <u>paralysing</u> fear. He knew that voice.

Page 37 Spelling

Q1 a) their

   b) there

   c) where

   d) whether

   e) bought

   f) quite

   g) practice

   h) effect

   i) stationary

   j) who's

Q2

Useful Words and Phrases for the Writing Question		
Starting a formal letter:	Ending a formal letter:	Beginning a speech:
Dear Sir / Madam Dear Mrs Jones	Yours sincerely Yours faithfully	Welcome Good evening
Persuasive phrases:	Impersonal phrases:	Phrases to link paragraphs
We all know that What we should do now Surely we could	It can be argued Some people believe One point of view is	On the other hand A second reason for this is Another important concern is

Writing Answers

Q3 <u>Occasionally</u>, I like to visit the centre of town. You can see all the <u>government</u> <u>buildings</u> which are really big and <u>impressive</u>. There are lots of <u>people</u> in the streets, walking and <u>laughing</u>. The <u>atmosphere's</u> brilliant. My favourite place is <u>definitely</u> the <u>cathedral</u> <u>which</u> is nine <u>hundred</u> years old. Inside the <u>cathedral</u> it's very cold but the <u>stained</u> glass <u>windows</u> are <u>beautiful</u>. There's also a coffee shop <u>there</u> which sells <u>delicious</u> cakes. <u>Separate</u> from the <u>cathedral</u> is a small chapel which is <u>notorious</u> for <u>having</u> nuns <u>buried</u> inside the walls.

Writing — Writing for Different Purposes

Page 38 Writing for the Reader or Audience

Q1 A ii) The text describes what happened in a fairly impersonal style and quotes an eye-witness to the event.

B iv) The text uses simple language and explains a word ("algae") that the younger children might not understand.

C i) The text uses an informal tone and language as if writing to a friend, e.g. "blimey", "did I tell you", "bigger than Gavin's bike."

D iii) The text uses formal and respectful language, and acknowledges that the reader knows a lot about the subject.

Q2 *Possible answer:*

12, Dogbowl Street
Harrogate
12th February

Dear Kate,

It was really exciting when I went to the zoo yesterday — this mad little kid let her hamster out into the puma cage! We were just wandering around and we heard a rumpus, so we rushed over to join the crowd outside the puma cage. The hamster was on the puma's back. You couldn't see what was happening very well, but apparently it was collecting the puma's fur in its pouches. The hamster was saved though, and the puma was alright too.

See you soon,

Gillian

Page 39 Writing for the Reader or Audience

Q1 iii) The headteacher and possibly readers of the local paper.

Q2 *Possible answers:*
<u>atmospheric</u> — The description of the holiday destination should give the feeling of what it's like to be there.
<u>fairly formal</u> — The entries are going to be read by the headteacher and possibly local newspaper readers so they shouldn't be too informal.
<u>positive</u> — The entries are about your favourite destination so they should be trying to show it in a good light.
<u>evocative</u> — The writing should give a good description so the reader can imagine what the place is like.

Q3 *e.g.*
The food in Brittany is wonderful. My family had never tasted anything better. You don't have to stick to the old French food clichés like croissants and baguettes. Instead you can go to markets which sell fresh fruit and honey pies which are delicious for breakfast. Bernadette and Hervé, the French couple we stayed with, went to the market every day. The weather was gorgeous, so you could wander idly around the market looking at the exquisite food and getting a suntan.

Page 40 Different Types of Writing

Q1

Type of Writing	Typical format / structure	Typical style/tone
Formal letter	Begins with an address and "Dear" Ends with "Yours sincerely" or "Yours faithfully"	Fairly formal and impersonal Written to specific reader(s)
Speech	Begins with a welcoming introduction, followed by paragraphs and conclusion.	Written as if speaking directly to audience
Article/report	Has a headline, sometimes written in columns	Informative and impersonal
Story	Standard format, in paragraphs, with a beginning, middle and end	Entertaining / imaginative
Leaflet	Headings breaking up text, pictures with captions	Informative or persuasive Usually fairly formal
Informal letter	Begins with "Dear..." Ends with informal sign-off, e.g. "Best wishes"	Personal, informal Written to specific reader(s)

Q2 *Possible answers:*

a) <u>Striking Binman Arrested</u>
A man was arrested in the city centre on Saturday for indecent exposure. Tim Hazelwood, a Thorncastle resident, marched through the city centre wearing a dustbin to raise publicity for the cause of binmen striking in the city.
  The binmen are striking for better pay to reflect their unpleasant job and unsociable working hours. The council have so far refused to offer a pay increase, claiming that there are more worthy causes deserving the council's money.

b) Dear Sandy Johns MP,
I am writing to you on behalf of the Refuse Collector's Strike Association of Thorncastle. We would like to request your support in our struggle for better pay. Please consider the fact that the job that refuse collectors perform is both very important and unpleasant. In addition to this the hours which we work are unsociable. These factors should be recognised with better pay.
Yours sincerely,
Jo Smith

c) <u>The Refuse Collector's Strike</u>
The refuse collectors of Thorncastle have decided to take strike action for better pay. The council believes that while the binmen have a worthy case, so do many other workers and the council's funds are limited. Negotiations are ongoing, and as little disruption will be caused as possible.
<u>What You Can Do To Help</u>
As rubbish is not being collected, it is necessary for us all to take steps to keep Thorncastle clean. Keeping bin bags outside your house is unhygienic — the council urges all Thorncastle residents to take rubbish to the skip themselves.

Page 41 Formal and Informal Writing

Q1 The answer should be fairly formal. On the one hand the speech is going to be given to a local MP and so can't be too informal in tone. On the other hand, the speech needs to be "light-hearted" so it can't be too formal either.

Q2 a) Good afternoon everyone. I'm here to tell you about events which have been happening in the school during the last few weeks. I will then show you around the school. You will have the chance to talk to some of the pupils and will be given some refreshments.

b) Switzerland is very exciting. There are many activities you can do, for example snowboarding, skiing, walking and shopping. In Basle there are bears you can feed, although it is quite cruel that they are kept in captivity.

c) The main lottery draw has been fixed three times in the last year, this newspaper can reveal. Our investigative reporter discovered that supporters of the governing party had won significant lottery sums on several different occasions.

Q3 *Possible answer:*
Dear Jo,

How are you? I was hoping you could give me some of your good advice. As you know, I've loved doing gymnastics for years and want to keep on doing it. However recently I've been stricken with rheumatism which is common among people as old as I am.

Before you retired, I seem to remember you spent some time as a homoeopathist. Do you have any recommendations for herbal remedies which might ease my pain and enable me to backflip again? I do hope you can help,
lots of love,
Bessie

Page 42 Writing to Inform, Explain and Describe

Q1 i) — it **explains** what to do
iii) — it **informs** the reader about what the place is like
v) — it **describes** the person and **explains** why they are important

Q2 a) 1, B
2, C
3, A

b) 1 — The text explains everything, e.g. "Orson Welles is a really important director." It doesn't assume that the audience have heard of the director or the film.
2 — The text assumes that the readers know a lot about the film already, e.g. it uses the phrase "as you know."
3 — The text acknowledges that the readers may know about the film, e.g. it uses the phrase "you have probably heard of."

Q3 *Example answer:*
My favourite film is called 'The Battle of Algiers' which was made in 1965 by the Italian director Gillo Pontecorvo. The film shows events in the Algerian Revolution which took place 1954-1962 against French colonial rule. It shows the cruelty of the French military, but also the devastation caused by terrorist bombs planted by the Algerian side.

One of the reasons I like the film is its documentary feel — it shows events in a very realistic way. There are no stars in the cast, and the black-and-white footage looks more like an old newsreel than a feature film. More importantly the film shows a very balanced view of the revolution — it isn't just propaganda for the winning side.

Page 43 Writing to Inform, Explain and Describe

Q1 a) In Normandy, there is a very beautiful valley called the Gorge Rancré. It has an unusually hot climate. This means that olive groves and vines can flourish there. Past the olive groves, there is a river which is known locally as the 'Devil's River'. The name originated in an ancient local myth that an animal had to be drowned in the river each year to keep the devil happy.

b) Henry VIII decided he wanted to get rid of Anne Boleyn because she had failed to bear him a son. This was important to Henry because he wanted a male heir to the throne. Therefore, charges of adultery were brought against Anne. These charges were probably untrue, but it didn't matter because Henry was so powerful. Anne was executed as a result.

Q2 a) exercises
b) delicious
c) incredibly
d) distant objects

Q3 a) The computer has a spell-checker which will find any incorrectly spelt words and help me change them.
b) My grandfather was an air-raid warden; he helped make sure people kept the black-out during air raids in World War II.
c) Liverpool is a multicultural city; people of many different cultures and faiths live there.
d) The striker was clearly offside — he had already run past all of the other players when the ball was passed to him.

Q4 *Possible answer:*
I rampaged over to the local funfair at the weekend. The rides were unbelievable. I tried the waltzer, but it made me feel unwell. Then I rode on the roller-coaster, and it was exhilarating. I loved going upside down and seeing all the people on the ground. When I got off the roller-coaster, I saw a friend from school but he disappeared before I could speak to him. Before I left, I devoured some candyfloss, which was gorgeous.

Page 44 Writing to Persuade, Argue and Advise

Q1 i, iii, iv

Q2 *Possible answers:*
a) People need to think about the effect smoking has on their health before they even try a cigarette.
b) The question we have to ask is, "If the government really has evidence about why we should eat spinach, why don't they tell us what it is?"
c) If you don't want to go on the trip, you should ask your mother to write a letter to the teacher explaining why.

Q3 *Possible answers:*
a) I enjoy swimming it is relaxing, fun and healthy.
b) It's important to read the newspapers because they are thought-provoking, informative and interesting.
c) We all know that homework is fascinating, inspiring and exciting.

Q4 *Possible answers:*
a) Perhaps you should take part in the race.
b) Maybe you could leave your job.
c) Would you like to come swimming at the leisure centre tomorrow?
d) Could you try to come to a decision soon?

Writing Answers

Page 45 Writing to Persuade, Argue and Advise

Q1 a) Paragraph (a) is not persuasive because it offers a fairly balanced view of the two candidates. It gives good points of both Claire Harris and Edward Jones.

b) Paragraph (b) is persuasive because it tries to persuade the reader that Claire Harris is the better candidate. It describes three of her good qualities for emphasis — that she is "intelligent, honest and cares about the local area." Her policies are praised, while in comparison her rival Edward Jones's track record is criticised.

Q2 a) The death penalty should not be reintroduced in Britain. There have been several recent cases in Britain where long-serving prisoners have been found innocent because of new evidence. If we had the death penalty in Britain these people would have been wrongly executed long ago. Lord Justice Hodgeman has said on this issue, "Although I have great faith in the British legal system, we should not lie to ourselves that it is infallible."

b) The death penalty should be reintroduced in Britain. Keeping people in prison costs the government money — for buildings, staff, food and healthcare. People who have committed horrific crimes and are sentenced to life imprisonment are wasting government resources. Re-introducing the death penalty would also act as a deterrent to criminals. It would show them that the legal system in Britain is strong and won't let them get away lightly with their crimes.

Q3 *Example answer:*
Despite protests from some parents and teachers, cars are still allowed in our school playground. This is a terrible hazard and we need to ask ourselves how much longer it can be allowed to continue.

The strongest argument against cars being allowed in the playground is that they are dangerous. Children run around in the playground, and the risk of an accident is high. There are several examples of children being run over and killed in school playgrounds. These tragedies are horrendous for the schools and families, and an appalling thing for other children to witness.

Some people argue that by driving slowly they can avoid having an accident. This is a misguided attitude. People are often killed or badly injured by cars driving as slowly as 20mph.

Another important reason for wanting to keep cars out of the playground is that they take up a lot of space. The playground is a useful area for children to run around, socialise and exercise. If they are kept in a small area of the playground then their breaktimes will be less healthy and stimulating.

In conclusion, teachers and parents who complain that there is no other space to park, or that their cars aren't safe elsewhere, aren't thinking about the safety and health of the children they claim to care for. We must support the campaign to keep cars out of the playground for good.

Page 46 Writing to Imagine, Explore and Entertain

Q1 iii) a gripping opening to the story

iv) development of the plot, characters and setting established in the opening.

ii) a crisis

i) a satisfying ending, which resolves the crisis

Q2 *Possible answers:*

a) Ilona turned to the headteacher furiously and screamed like a banshee.

b) As he crept over to the side of the ship, Bob's shoes squeaked like mice.

c) The atmosphere in the dentist's waiting room was like a funeral parlour.

d) The chips looked gorgeous. Henry was as hungry as a lion.

Q3 *Possible answers:*

a) Slashing rain set off a summer storm.

b) Cool, calm and collected, the cat crept through the casino.

Q4 *Possible answers:*

a) crash, bang, boom

b) screech, zoom, growl

Q5 *Possible answer:*
Then, making the whole situation worse — into the room marched my old nemesis Miss Rumpel! I was so shocked my entire body went numb. There was no chance of hiding, so I had to confront her. I took the catapult from my pocket, saying to myself, "It's not over until I'm given double detention for the next six years."

Q6 a) Henry — athletic, timid, fit, introverted

b) Mrs Henderson — intimidating, ancient, garrulous, authoritarian

c) Pau — fashionable, famous, glamorous, musical

Page 47 Writing to Imagine, Explore and Entertain

Q1 Paragraph (ii) is more suspenseful. This is because it withholds the information about what is in the bag until the end of the paragraph. Paragraph (i) lets you know what's in the bag straight away, so there isn't any suspense.

Q2 a) She was sitting quietly on a bench in the park. She didn't seem scared. I rushed up and said, "Run away — as fast as you can," but she didn't seem to understand.

b) The warrior Xenodwarf wielded his sword and yelled, "Enemy, prepare for death." To his surprise the enemy refused to surrender and did a nifty flying kick towards his right ear.

Q3 I was led through the servants' quarters towards the big kitchens. I felt scared, and couldn't stop my hands from shaking. The only time I'd been here before had been to deliver a message to my sister who worked here as a lady's maid. Even then, I'd been frightened. There were stories about the manor; people I knew in the village said there were so many corridors under the house it was like a maze. A boy had been lost down there, in a game of hide and seek. The rumour was that he was still alive.

Q4 *Example answer:*
Dear Claire,
That video you lent me got me into all sorts of trouble! I took it with me on my last voyage. After I'd learnt the basic moves, I found I was pretty good at it. The music was so infectiously jolly and toe-tapping. It reached the point though where I was finding it really difficult to steer the boat, because I was so busy dancing. I guess you could almost call it an addiction.

Well, all was not lost, because what should I find under a life jacket but my favourite Bach CD. That CD saved me — I was so relieved to listen to something calm and classical. So three months later than expected, here I am

Writing Answers

back at home. Hope to see you soon dear — but you'd better not lend me any more videos!
Best wishes,
Sterling

Q5 *Example answer:*
July 14th
Gemma's wedding today was beautiful. I felt really proud of her. She let me be a bridesmaid which was fun — even if the dress I had to wear was horrific. My mum and dad really enjoyed the ceremony too, which I was relieved about because they were getting really stressed about all the arrangements.

I remember when I first met Gemma's fiancé Geoffrey, I wasn't sure whether I liked him. His musical taste was awful and he tried to make me laugh with jokes which weren't funny. To be honest, I still don't feel that I know him very well.

When I heard that they were getting married, I was a bit shocked. Gemma's only a few years older than me, but by getting married she seemed like an old woman. Now they're getting a mortgage on a house and Gemma's going to move out. I've never lived without my sister before, and the idea of it makes me feel a bit worried. I'll be left living with just my parents and that won't be as much fun at all.

Page 48 *Writing to Analyse, Review and Comment*

Q1 a) Children over 14 should be allowed to go on holiday by themselves because they enjoy different holiday activities to their parents.

   b) The advertising by confectionery and fast-food manufacturers on children's television persuades children to eat unhealthy food.

   c) Few people are aware that the government is trying to introduce stealth taxes on mobile phones.

Q2 *Possible answers:*

   a) <u>Some people believe that</u> the greenhouse effect is having a terrible effect on the Earth's environment.

   b) <u>One point of view is that</u> if the Green Party got into power, it would be great for Britain and great for the environment.

   c) Dogs <u>often</u> make very good pets, because they force people to go for walks and get some fresh air.

   d) Trains are <u>usually</u> not on time.

Q3 *Example answer:*
<u>Controversy Over Football Stadium Plans</u>
There are arguments raging in Sudley about whether a new football stadium should be built in the centre of the city.

The managers of the local football club are pushing for the plans to go ahead. They argue that the stadium will be much bigger than the old one. This will allow more fans to watch the match, and also bring in more money.

However, not everyone is so keen. Some local residents are worried about the noise and traffic congestion which might be caused by placing the new stadium in the centre of town. There are also fears about football hooliganism.

Local shopkeepers and businesses support the idea though. They hope it will bring more people into the town centre. Pubs and food outlets in particular might profit.

The council are finding it hard to come to a decision about planning permission, when the people affected have such different points of view.

Page 49 *Writing to Analyse, Review and Comment*

Q1 *Possible answer:*
Arguments supporting YES
1. Tax-payers' money shouldn't be given to support a family who are already rich.
2. The members of the Royal Family are no different to anybody else — they just happen to have been born into a very rich and powerful family.
3. The monarch shouldn't be head of state, because they aren't elected. The Royal Family isn't democratic.
Arguments supporting NO
1. Tradition is important, the Royal Family have played an important role in the history of Britain.
2. The Royal Family play an important role as the figureheads of various charities and good causes.
3. The Royal Family are something famous about Britain. Their palaces and appearances attract tourism.

Q2 a) This conclusion is too vague, e.g. "It's a really difficult issue and it's hard to reach a conclusion." It fails to make a memorable statement about the issue and doesn't make the writer's viewpoint clear.

   b) This is a good conclusion. It refers back to the bulk of the essay, gives the writer's viewpoint and ends on a strong statement. The tone is fairly impersonal and objective.

   c) This conclusion doesn't work because it allows the writer's personal opinion to take over completely. This means that the tone of the writing becomes personal and subjective, e.g. "any other views are deeply misguided."

Q3 *Possible answer:*
The Royal Family are a really contentious issue. As discussed above, some people strongly believe that they still have a role in modern Britain while others see them as an out-dated drain on resources. I believe that the Royal Family should retain their traditional role as head of state, but with less privileges. For example some of the palaces could be given to the National Trust and be used to attract more tourism. However, any change would be a surprise, as at the moment the Royals seem as popular as ever.

Writing — Text Structure and Organisation

Page 50 *Paragraphs*

Q1   1 — a
         2 — d
         3 — c
         4 — e
         5 — b

Q2 Pompeii was a small city of no great importance in the Roman world. One of the few mentions it gets in ancient texts is in relation to a fight which broke out at the amphitheatre in which several people were killed. We can glean more information from the archaeological excavations at the site. From the size of the site it is estimated that it had about twenty thousand inhabitants.

Writing Answers

Evidence from the site includes: buildings, the contents of people's houses, wall paintings, graffiti and plaster casts of people who died in the explosion.

Q3 As Myrna sat down at the kitchen table she already felt full. So far she had eaten five blueberry tarts, ten Easter eggs, a rhubarb crumble and 76 fun-size chocolate bars.
    Ali ran into the room and saw the last piece of evidence, the double-cream layered pavlova still there on the kitchen table.
    "Come on, he's almost here!" he yelled.
    "I'm trying," groaned Myrna.
    Meanwhile, the dastardly Mr Smiker was walking slowly across the fields, his nose twitching in the breeze. The unmistakable scent of a missing double-cream layered pavlova filled his monstrous nostrils. He smiled a terrifying smile. Even his teeth were evil.

Page 51 Paragraphs

Q1 We all know that school buses are environmentally friendly. If our school bus was discontinued each child would have to travel to school individually. Seventy-five students make use of the bus service; that's a lot of extra cars. As the headteacher has said, "The pollution caused by the extra cars travelling to school would have a bad effect on the environment."

Q2 a) Some people are strongly against abortion.

   b) Some people support a woman's right to have an abortion.

Q3 Once, when Hilary was at primary school, she'd climbed over the playing field fence. All her friends had run away because they were scared. Hilary had refused to be scared and had started walking as far from school as possible. After about two hours she had reached her own house. Hilary had been annoyed; she'd wanted to have an adventure, not to go home.

Q4 Paragraph (a) compares the two seasons better, because it gives some detail about each one. Paragraph (b) is almost all about winter, and gives very little detail about summer, so it isn't a proper comparison.

Q5 *Example answer:*
The activities you can do in cities and in the countryside are very different. Cities have lots of fun places to go, for example, museums, theatres and cinemas. In the countryside there aren't as many places like this. On the other hand there are lots of outdoor activities you can do, for example walking and horse-riding.

Page 52 Linking Paragraphs

Q1 furthermore, another point of view is, with hindsight, a contrasting view is, however, another example of, in addition to this, on the other hand

Q2 a) Nowadays, however, people know that white lead is dangerous.

   b) On the other hand, the Parent's Association have a fairly moderate view.

   c) However, the views of many parents about cartoons contrast strongly with those of their children.

Q3 *Example answer:*
When I was ten I lived in Newcastle. It's a big city, and you can get around it by Metro. In the area I lived, called Jesmond, there was a dene (park) you could run around which had a river and pet's corner.

While I was living in Newcastle, I went to school at 'All Saints' primary school. The school was in temporary accommodation, so most of the classrooms were in portacabins.

Q4 *Example answer:*
I think that fashion can be as outrageous as you want. What you wear shows what your personality is like. For example, I wear an Alkaline Trio hoodie that I got from one of their gigs because it's cool and it shows what music I'm into.
On the other hand, you could look at my parents' idea of fashion. They're really conformist and buy clothes from catalogues and Marks and Spencer. They wear their clothes for years. If they buy new clothes they always choose ones identical to what they had before.

Page 53 Writing Good Introductions

Q1 **ii)** Good evening
    iv) We are here tonight to discuss
    viii) Welcome
    x) The key issue I am going to discuss is

Q2 Paragraph **i)** is persuasive. It argues clearly in favour of more security in schools. Paragraph **ii)** on the other hand describes different points of view as if they are equally valid — this would be appropriate for an analysing essay, but not for a persuasive essay.

Q3 *Example answer:*
    The issue of whether advertising should be allowed on children's television is a controversial one. Many parents argue that the adverts should be banned, because they persuade their children to want expensive toys and unhealthy food. On the other hand, television executives argue that the money from advertising is spent producing good children's programming. They also point to the fact that many children enjoy watching adverts because of their imagination and humour. This essay will discuss both sides of the argument.

Q4 *Example answer:*
    Bob was feeling happy. He had a date with Karen tonight down at the SuperBowl — it was the over-50s discount night so they could have two games for the price of one. He turned on some Tom Jones and opened the wardrobe to find his favourite viscose shirt. He blinked; he gulped. All his clothes were torn to shreds. Then, downstairs, he heard the noise.

Page 54 Structuring the Middle Bit

Q1 v) Introduction — outline your main argument.

   i) Give a reason to support your argument. Back it up with evidence.

   vi) Give a second reason to support you argument. Back it up with evidence.

   iii) Give a reason why people might not agree with your argument. Give evidence of why they are wrong.

   iv) Give a second reason why people might not agree with your argument. Give evidence of why they are wrong.

   ii) Conclusion — bring together main points why your argument's right.

Q2 Essay plan **ii)** is the worst structured of the three. It only gives advantages to living in the countryside, and doesn't comment on the disadvantages. Therefore it isn't a

Writing Answers

balanced essay, and appears to be biased towards living in the countryside.

Q3 ii), iii), i), iv)

Page 55 _Structuring the Middle Bit_

Q1 a) • The SATs will be over soon
  • Hard work will be rewarded with good grades
  • Pupils who don't work hard will regret it later.

b) _Example answer:_
The SATs Will Be Over Soon
  • The SATs will be over in a week.
  • There will be a long summer holiday soon.
All Your Hard Work Will Be Rewarded With Good Grades
  • Hard work is the only way to guarantee good grades.
  • It will make you feel a sense of achievement when you get good grades.
Pupils Who Don't Work Hard Will Regret It Later
  • If you don't work hard, you won't get good grades
  • You will feel like a nitwit when you get your results back.

Q2 _Example answer:_

a) Arguments supporting your point of view
  • If a driver runs over a pedestrian when he's doing 20mph, there is a one in five chance they will be killed
  • City speed limits are often as high as 30mph — the risk to lives is too high.
Opinions which disagree with your point of view
  • People are often in a hurry, they don't want to slow down
  • Improvements in traffic control and pedestrian crossings make the roads safer, and allow cars to go faster.

b) Arguments supporting your point of view
  • Reducing the number of road deaths is much more important than people's need to travel to places quickly.
  • Road accidents can be tragic, and cause a lot of pain and grief.
Opinions which disagree with your point of view
  • Most drivers are responsible and would slow down if there was a hazard.
  • The focus should be on punishing people who break the existing speed limits — they are the drivers who cause accidents. They would still go fast even if you reduced the speed limit.

c) Arguments supporting your point of view
  3. If a driver runs over a pedestrian when he's doing 20mph, there is a one in five chance they will be killed
  4. City speed limits are often as high as 30mph — the risk to lives is too high.
  1. Reducing the number of road deaths is much more important than people's need to travel to places quickly.
  2. Road accidents can be tragic, and cause a lot of pain and grief.
Opinions which disagree with your point of view
  • ~~People are often in a hurry, they don't want to slow down~~
  1. Improvements in traffic control and pedestrian crossings make the roads safer, and allow cars to go faster.
  2. Most drivers are responsible and would slow down if

there was a hazard.
3. The focus should be on punishing people who break the existing speed limits — they are the drivers who cause accidents. They would still go fast even if you reduced the speed limit.

Page 56 _Pointing Out the Structure for the Reader_

Q1 Introduction **ii)** signposts clearly what the structure of the leaflet is going to be. It says specifically which three areas are going to be covered by the leaflet.

Q2 ii) The second half of this essay will discuss the disadvantages...

  iv) There are three main issues at stake here; they will be discussed in turn.

  v) The first half of this essay will discuss the advantages...

  vi) The second reason for supporting this point of view...

  vii) Finally, this essay will consider the impact on...

Q3 A big argument in favour of the new sports hall is that it is a major facility that the school currently lacks. At the moment children have to travel to the local leisure centre to do P.E. and this is a waste of valuable lesson time.
  A second important argument in favour of the new sports hall is that exercise is a really important part of education. It helps make people healthy and happy. It would be good if the school could offer a wider range of sporting activities and a new sports hall would enable this.
  The second half of this essay will discuss the disadvantages to the new sports hall. Firstly, the proposed site for the new sports hall is far from ideal. The plan is to build it on the site of the old and beautiful school garden. Many people disagree with this strongly.
  Another reason people don't want the school garden destroyed is that is the only place, other than the playground, where children can sit and relax at breaktimes. The importance of a peaceful place in a busy school cannot be dismissed lightly.

Page 57 _Writing Good Conclusions_

Q1 This statement is false. The conclusion should bring together the points made in the essay; it shouldn't bring in new information. It's also very important that the conclusion matches the tone and opinion of the rest of the essay.

Q2 **i)** a final statement about the topic
  iii) a summary of the main points in your essay
  viii) your own view on the topic

Q3 _Example answer:_
In conclusion, animal testing is cruel and often unnecessary. Testing causes pain to the animals. In the case of cosmetics testing this seems particularly unnecessary, as they could be tested on humans instead. Although there may be some worth in testing medicines, I still believe it should be kept to a minimum. Any unnecessary testing should be banned.

Q4 _Example answer:_
Velma picked up the axe, and walked down the stairs to the cellar. Bob slammed the door behind her and locked it. Velma yelled in indignation. He ran to the phone and dialled 999. There was a crash as Velma swung the axe against the cellar door. Bob was green with fear.
  Then Karen walked in.

Writing Answers

"Thank heavens you're here," cried Bob.
"What's the trouble?" said Karen.
Velma crashed through the cellar door. Karen whacked her over the head with her bowling ball.
"Come on Bob," said Karen, "we've got a date."

Writing — Practice Questions

Page 58 The Long Writing Question

Q1 a) ii) a mixture of teachers, pupils and parents

b) "Write an article for your school magazine"

Q2 a) formal, polite

b) It should be fairly formal because it is going to be read by parents and teachers, and is trying to discuss an issue seriously. It should be polite, because appearing angry and offensive won't help to persuade people round to your point of view. Teachers and parents are more likely to respond well to a polite, formal tone.

Q3 a) to persuade, argue or advise

b) It means that the purpose of the article is to argue in favour of one point of view and to persuade the readers that this view is right.

Page 59 The Long Writing Question

Q1 a) ii) homework is an important issue / I believe that / should pupils be given less homework?

b) Option i) is phrases suitable for a speech, not an article. Option iii) is too informal, plus you shouldn't insult people who don't agree with your view.

Option iv) is suitable for an informative essay, not a persuasive essay.
Option ii) is best because the tone is fairly formal, and the phrases are suitable for a persuasive article.

Q2 Use the phrases from your answer to Q1 a) and some of your own, e.g.
• We all know that
• We all need to think hard about
• The essay is going to argue that
• In conclusion

Q3 Example answer:

a) • Homework makes pupils stressed and tired.
• Homework stops children from taking part in extra-curricular activities.

b) • Teachers often set homework from habit, even if it isn't really necessary.
• Teachers often underestimate how long homework tasks will take pupils to do.

Q4 Example answer:

a) • Homework lets pupils practise skills.
• Homework helps pupils learn information

b) • Homework helps children learn the skill of working on their own, and managing work in their own time.

• It means revision for exams is easier, because the children will have learnt more during the year.

Page 60 The Long Writing Question

Q1 **a)-c)** *Example answer:*
Reasons you agree/disagree with homework
2. Homework makes pupils stressed and tired.
1. Homework stops children from taking part in extra-curricular activities.
• Teachers often set homework from habit, even if it isn't really necessary.
3. Teachers often underestimate how long homework tasks will take pupils to do. (3 goes with 1)

Different opinions people might have about homework
1. Homework lets pupils practise skills. (1 goes with 2)
2. Homework helps pupils learn information.
4. Homework helps children learn the skill of working on their own, and managing work in their own time.
3. It means revision for exams is easier, because the children will have learnt more during the year.

Q2 Options i) and ii) are both good. Option iii) isn't very good because it is always necessary to consider both points of view.

Q3 This statement is false. It's OK to change your argument but you should say you're doing it and mention it again in the conclusion.

Q4 *A good answer will:*
• *Use the essay plan:*
— *discuss the points in the essay plan*
— *give priority to the points that are marked as the most important in the essay plan*
— *use some of the words and phrases in the 'words and phrases to begin and end your essay' box in the introduction and conclusion.*
• *Structure the essay well:*
— *clear introduction, middle paragraphs and conclusion*
— *structured middle section, e.g. points supporting your opinion discussed first, points against your opinion (and why they're wrong) discussed second.*
• *Make the essay flow well:*
— *link paragraphs together smoothly*
— *signpost the structure for the reader*
• *Use evidence to back up points:*
— *Each paragraph should have a clear point backed up with evidence, e.g. quotes, statistics, examples.*
• *Use correct punctuation, spelling and grammar:*
— *use a variety of punctuation correctly, e.g. question marks, apostrophes, exclamation marks and commas*
— *punctuate long sentences correctly using commas, semicolons or colons.*
• *Use interesting vocabulary and sentence structures:*
— *include some unusual and longer words*
— *use a variety of verbs*
— *vary length of sentences*
— *vary how you start sentences*
• *Use persuasive tricks:*
— *e.g. rhetorical questions, groups of three adjectives, use "we" and "us", be polite*
• *Use a tone suitable to the audience / reader:*
— *the article is for readers of the school magazine, including parents and teachers, so it should be fairly formal and polite in tone.*
• *Be about 300 words long*

Q5 *I can't help you with this one, lazybones.*

Writing Answers

Page 61 The Short Writing Question

Q1 <u>What is the purpose of this piece of writing?</u>
to entertain and imagine
<u>Who is going to read it?</u>
readers of the local Herald newspaper
<u>Write down three words which describe the tone you think the writing should have</u>
Possible answers: lighthearted, informal, humorous

Q2 a) • the characters who are mistaken for each other and why they are so alike
• who mixes them up
• what the result of the mix up is

b) *Example answer:*
• <u>the characters who are mistaken for each other and why they are so alike</u>
— Shaun and Jason
— They are two brothers from Cheshire who look a bit alike. They're so boring people can't tell them apart.
• <u>who mixes them up</u>
— A mad professor called Pete who's been inventing a new type of witchcraft for three years.
• <u>what the result of the mix up is</u>
— Pete meets Shaun. He is so bored that he performs a spell to try and get rid of the boringness.
— Jason turns up.
— Pete thinks his spell's gone wrong and the boringness is expanding. He is so scared that he jumps in the canal.
— Jason and Shaun haul Pete out of the canal.
— They are in the local paper as heroes. No one thinks they're boring any more.

Q3 *A good answer will:*
• <u>Use the essay plan:</u>
— *use the structure and ideas thought out in the essay plan*
• <u>Structure the writing well:</u>
— *write in paragraphs*
— *structure your story in an effective way, e.g. introduction, development of characters and situation, crisis, conclusion which resolves the crisis.*
• <u>Make the essay flow well:</u>
— *link paragraphs together smoothly*
• <u>Use correct punctuation, spelling and grammar:</u>
— *use a variety of punctuation correctly, e.g. question marks, apostrophes, exclamation marks and commas*
— *punctuate long sentences correctly using commas, semicolons or colons.*
• <u>Use interesting vocabulary and sentence structures:</u>
— *include some unusual and longer words*
— *use a variety of verbs*
— *vary length of sentences*
— *vary how you start sentences*
• <u>Use tricks for good imaginative writing:</u>
— *Build up atmosphere and mood, by using description and imagery, e.g. similes and metaphors, adjectives and adverbs, alliteration and onomatopoeia.*
— *Use suspense and surprise to keep the reader interested.*
— *Perhaps write from the point of view of one of the characters in the story.*

— *Avoid using clichés*
• <u>Use a tone suitable to the audience and purpose of the writing:</u>
— *e.g. lighthearted, inoffensive, humorous*
• <u>Be about 200 words long</u>

Q4 *This one's up to you.*

Page 62 Revision Questions

Q1-3 *Good answers to these three questions will:*
• <u>Have completed a rough essay plan:</u>
— *For Q1 and Q2 an essay plan based on the planning page provided should have been completed. It should include points made in the question, and your own ideas.*
— *For Q3 a rough plan should have been sketched out, including points made in the question.*
• <u>The writing should use the essay plan:</u>
— *discuss the points in the essay plan*
— *use the structure thought out in the essay plan*
• <u>Structure the essay well:</u>
— *clear introduction, middle paragraphs and conclusion*
— *structured middle section*
• <u>Make the essay flow well:</u>
— *link paragraphs together smoothly*
— *signpost the structure for the reader*
• <u>Use evidence to back up points:</u>
— *Each paragraph should have a clear point backed up with evidence, e.g. quotes, statistics, examples.*
• <u>Use correct punctuation, spelling and grammar:</u>
— *use a variety of punctuation correctly, e.g. question marks, apostrophes, exclamation marks and commas*
— *punctuate long sentences correctly using commas, semicolons or colons.*
• <u>Use interesting vocabulary and sentence structures:</u>
— *include some unusual and longer words*
— *use a variety of verbs*
— *vary length of sentences*
— *vary how you start sentences*
• <u>Make the writing suitable for the writing purpose</u>
Q1 — a piece of informative writing
Q2 — a piece of analytical writing
Q3 — a piece of persuasive writing
• <u>Use a tone suitable to the audience / reader:</u>
Q1 — readers of a broadsheet newspaper
Q2 — pupils at your school
Q3 — managing director of local theatre
• <u>Be the right length</u>
— *Q1 and Q2 are long writing questions, so they should be about 300 words long*
— *Q3 is a short writing question, so it should be about 200 words long.*

Shakespeare Answers

Shakespeare — The Basics

N.B. All answers are merely suggestions — many alternatives are possible.

Page 63 Know Your Play

Q1 a) Richard III

Act 1 Scene 1 — Richard pretends to support Clarence and plans to become King after Edward IV, who's ill, dies.

Act 1 Scene 2 — Richard persuades Anne to marry him.

Act 1 Scene 3 — Richard argues about power with Queen Elizabeth and her family, then Queen Margaret says they're fighting over what's hers and curses them. Richard gives two murderers instructions to kill Clarence.

Act 1 Scene 4 — The murderers kill Clarence.

Act 2 Scene 1 — King Edward gets Queen Elizabeth to make peace with Buckingham and Hastings. Richard announces that Clarence is dead and blames Queen Elizabeth's relatives. He makes King Edward feel guilty about Clarence's death.

Act 2 Scene 2 — Queen Elizabeth announces that King Edward is dead. Buckingham and Richard plan to separate the young Prince Edward, who is next in line to the throne, from his family.

Act 2 Scene 3 — Three citizens discuss England's future and the danger posed by Richard.

Act 2 Scene 4 — Queen Elizabeth is told that her relatives, Rivers and Grey, and her ally Vaughan, have been arrested by Richard and Buckingham. She and the Duke of York (her youngest son) go to sanctuary to be safe from Richard.

Act 3 Scene 1 — Queen Elizabeth's son, the young Prince Edward, arrives in the Tower, and his brother the Duke of York is brought there too from sanctuary. Richard doesn't trust Hastings but says he'll reward Buckingham for his loyalty.

Act 3 Scene 2 — Hastings tells Catesby he won't support Richard's bid to be King. Stanley warns Hastings about the danger from Richard, but Hastings isn't worried.

Act 3 Scene 3 — Rivers, Grey and Vaughan are executed.

Act 3 Scene 4 — Richard says Hastings is a traitor and orders his execution.

Act 3 Scene 5 — Richard and Buckingham trick the mayor into supporting them. Hastings is dead.

Act 3 Scene 6 — A scrivener says Hastings was unfairly accused of being a traitor.

Act 3 Scene 7 — Richard agrees to be King, after initially pretending to be reluctant about it.

Act 4 Scene 1 — Elizabeth and her family are refused permission to visit the young Princes in the Tower.

Act 4 Scene 2 — King Richard plots the deaths of the young Princes and his new wife Anne, so that he can marry Queen Elizabeth's daughter. Buckingham is out of Richard's favour and plans to get away from him.

Act 4 Scene 3 — The young Princes and Anne are all dead. Richmond and Buckingham are raising armies to fight Richard.

Act 4 Scene 4 — Richard persuades Queen Elizabeth to let him marry her daughter. Richmond's army is approaching, and Richard doesn't trust Stanley.

Act 4 Scene 5 — Stanley secretly supports Richmond.

Act 5 Scene 1 — Buckingham is executed.

Act 5 Scene 2 — Richmond is optimistic about the battle.

Act 5 Scene 3 — The ghosts of Richard's victims wish death on Richard and success to Richmond. Richmond and Richard give speeches to their troops before battle.

Act 5 Scene 4 — Richard tries to find Richmond so he can fight him in the battle.

Act 5 Scene 5 — Richmond kills Richard and Stanley presents Richmond with the crown. Richmond plans a peaceful future for England.

Much Ado About Nothing

Act 1 Scene 1 — Claudio says he's in love with Hero. Don Pedro says he'll set them up.

Act 1 Scene 2 — Antonio thinks Don Pedro loves Hero, and tells Leonato.

Act 1 Scene 3 — Don John decides to spoil the relationship.

Act 2 Scene 1 — At the dance, Don John tricks Claudio into thinking Don Pedro's after Hero for himself, but he fails as Don Pedro puts Claudio straight. Don Pedro and Leonato decide to set up Benedick and Beatrice.

Act 2 Scene 2 — Borachio tells Don John how he can ruin the wedding by making it look like Hero's having an affair.

Act 2 Scene 3 — Don Pedro, Leonato and Claudio trick Benedick into thinking Beatrice is in love with him.

Act 3 Scene 1 — Hero and Ursula trick Beatrice into thinking Benedick is in love with her.

Act 3 Scene 2 — Benedick is obviously in love, but denies it. Don John tells Claudio he can prove that Hero's having an affair.

Act 3 Scene 3 — The Watch overhear Borachio and Conrade talking about the trick, and arrest them.

Act 3 Scene 4 — Margaret and Hero chat about the wedding. Then Margaret teases Beatrice about Benedick.

Act 3 Scene 5 — Dogberry and Verges try to tell Leonato about their arrest, but Leonato's in a hurry and won't listen to them.

Act 4 Scene 1 — At the wedding, Claudio says he won't marry Hero because she's not a virgin. Leonato's really upset and says he wishes Hero was dead, but the Friar says the best thing is to pretend she's dead until things calm down. Benedick and Beatrice tell each other that they're in love. Beatrice is sure Hero's innocent, and gets Benedick to promise to challenge Claudio to a duel.

Act 4 Scene 2 — Dogberry, Verges and the Sexton interview the prisoners.

Act 5 Scene 1 — Leonato and Claudio have a big argument, and Benedick challenges Claudio to a duel. Then Borachio owns up to the trick. Leonato says he'll forgive Claudio if he agrees to marry Antonio's daughter (who doesn't really exist).

Act 5 Scene 2 — Beatrice and Benedick admit their love in a roundabout sort of way. Ursula tells them that Hero's been proved innocent.

Act 5 Scene 3 — Claudio grieves for Hero at her tomb.

Act 5 Scene 4 — Hero turns up alive and well at the wedding, and she and Claudio get married. Benedick and Beatrice decide to get married too.

The Tempest

Act 1 Scene 1 — The ship carrying Alonso and his followers is caught in a violent storm.

Shakespeare Answers

Act 1 Scene 2 — On the island, Prospero, who raised the storm with his magic, tells Miranda that, in the past, Antonio and Alonso robbed him of his title of Duke of Milan and set him and Miranda adrift at sea, with only Gonzalo helping them. Ferdinand arrives and he and Miranda fall in love straightaway, but Prospero decides to test their love and make things difficult for them.

Act 2 Scene 1 — Alonso believes Ferdinand must have drowned in the storm. Antonio persuades Sebastian to kill Alonso while he is sleeping, so that Sebastian can become King of Naples, but Ariel arrives just in time to stop them.

Act 2 Scene 2 — Trinculo meets Caliban when he tries to take shelter under Caliban's cloak. Stephano, who is drunk, finds them and gives Caliban some wine, and Caliban thinks Stephano must be a god.

Act 3 Scene 1 — Miranda comforts Ferdinand as he piles up logs as ordered by Prospero. Miranda and Ferdinand agree to get married.

Act 3 Scene 2 — Stephano, Trinculo and Caliban are all drunk, and Stephano beats up Trinculo when Ariel makes it seem that Trinculo is calling him a liar. Caliban tells Stephano that, if he kills Prospero, Stephano can have Miranda and be 'King of the island', and Stephano agrees to do it.

Act 3 Scene 3 — Ariel makes a magic banquet appear in front of Alonso and his followers, before making it suddenly vanish. He also tells them that the shipwreck was their punishment for throwing Prospero out of Milan. Alonso is sure Ferdinand is dead, and Gonzalo tries to keep everyone calm.

Act 4 Scene 1 — Prospero says Ferdinand and Miranda can get married and they watch some spirits perform a masque to celebrate. Then Prospero suddenly remembers the plot to kill him, and Prospero and Ariel chase off Caliban, Stephano and Trinculo.

Act 5 Scene 1 — Prospero casts a final spell on Alonso and his followers before forgiving them all, and revealing that Ferdinand is alive and engaged to Miranda. The Boatswain arrives and says the ship is fine, and Prospero invites them all back to his cave before they all set off home. Stephano, Trinculo and Caliban get told off and ordered to tidy Prospero's cave. Ariel is set free once he's arranged good weather for the journey.

Epilogue — Prospero asks for the audience's support on his journey back to Milan.

---

b) Richard III

Act 1 — Richard persuades Anne to marry him and has Clarence killed.

Act 2 — King Edward dies and Buckingham plans to separate the young Prince Edward from his family. Richard arrests Rivers, Grey and Vaughan, so Queen Elizabeth and the Duke of York (her youngest son) flee to sanctuary.

Act 3 — The young Princes are brought to the Tower and Richard has Rivers, Grey, Vaughan and Hastings killed. Richard and Buckingham trick the Mayor into supporting Richard's claim to the throne. Richard initially pretends to be reluctant, but then agrees to become King.

Act 4 — Richard has the young Princes and Anne killed and plans to marry Elizabeth's daughter. Buckingham is out of Richard's favour. Richmond and Buckingham are raising armies against Richard.

Act 5 — Buckingham is executed, and the ghosts of Richard's victims wish death upon him. Richmond kills Richard in the battle and becomes King.

Much Ado About Nothing

Act 1 — Claudio's in love with Hero, and Don Pedro says he'll chat her up for Claudio. Don John plans to ruin the relationship.

Act 2 — At the dance, Don John tells Claudio that Don Pedro wants Hero for himself, and Claudio falls for it at first, but is put straight by Don Pedro. Borachio and Don John plan how to make it seem like Hero's having an affair. Leonato, Don Pedro and Claudio trick Benedick into thinking Beatrice loves him.

Act 3 — Hero and Ursula trick Beatrice into thinking Benedick loves her. Don John tells Claudio Hero's having an affair. The Watch arrest Conrade and Borachio.

Act 4 — Claudio rejects Hero at their wedding.

Act 5 — Don John's trick is exposed. Claudio marries Hero, and Benedick and Beatrice get married too.

The Tempest

Act 1 — Alonso and his followers are caught in a storm and washed up on a remote island. Prospero tells Miranda that Alonso and Antonio betrayed him in the past, and Miranda and Ferdinand fall in love.

Act 2 — Antonio and Sebastian plot to kill Alonso. Trinculo, Caliban and Stephano meet.

Act 3 — Miranda and Ferdinand agree to marry, and Caliban persuades Stephano to kill Prospero. Ariel plays a magic trick on Alonso and his followers.

Act 4 — Prospero says Miranda and Ferdinand can get married, then goes off to deal with Caliban, Stephano and Trinculo.

Act 5 — Prospero forgives his enemies and gives up his magic. The characters prepare to set off home.

Q2, Q3, Q4 *Answers to these questions depend on which play you're studying.*

Q5 a) A long section of a play

b) A shorter section of a play — part of an act

c) One of the people in the play

d) A play that ends badly for the main character

e) A play that is funny or has a happy ending

f) A play about people in the past

g) A group of words with a set rhythm

h) A long bit of talking by one person

i) Part of a sentence

j) Any dialogue that's not poetry — normal speech

k) Dialogue in separate lines with a rhythm

l) The rhythm of poetry

m) When a character leaves the stage

n) When all of the characters present leave the stage

o) When a character says something that the other characters can't hear

Shakespeare Answers

Page 64 Understanding the Language

Q1
thy — your
ere — before
thee — you
thou wilt — you will
hither — to here
he hath — he has
hie — go
thou art — you are
thou hast — you have
wherefore — why
hence — from here
thou — you

Q2 a) a type of perfume

b) be better than, surpass

c) bootless — pointless, useless
prophesy — foresee, predict

d) corpse, dead body

Page 65 Understanding the Language

Q1 Possible answer:
• HASTINGS Oh poor England! But I don't deserve the slightest sympathy — if I hadn't been so stupid I could have avoided this. Stanley warned me that Richard was dangerous, but I thought I knew better and scoffed at the idea of running away. Even my horse tripped up three times today and looked scared when it looked at the tower — as if it was trying to avoid leading me to my death.

Q2 Possible answer:
• BENEDICK I've put up with more abuse from her than a wooden block could have stood. An old lifeless tree would have answered her back — even my mask came to life and argued with her. She told me, not realising she was talking to me, that I was a clown, and that I was more boring than watching ice melt. She was making fun of me over and over again, to the point where I felt like I was standing in front of a target being shot at by a whole army. Every word she says is like a dagger. If her breath was as horrid as her words are, everyone around her would drop dead. I wouldn't marry her even if she were the richest person in the world.

Q3 Possible answer:
• PROSPERO Look, it's me, Prospero — the man who was Duke of Milan but had it stolen from him. If you need more proof that it's me, I'm going to hug you, and warmly welcome you and your friends.

Q4 *This answer depends on which play you're doing.*

Page 66 Backing Up Your Answers

Q1 a) • poor man

b) • I am a plain-dealing villain.

c) • most wicked sir, whom to call brother / Would even infect my mouth, I do forgive

d) • Thy garments are not spotted with our blood

e) • moonshine

• green sour ringlets
• the ewe
• midnight mushrooms
• noontide sun
• mutinous winds
• green sea
• azured vault

Page 67 Backing Up Your Answers

Q1 a) • Go, by this token

b) • thou mayst brain him
• Batter his skull with a log
• paunch him with a stake
• cut his wezand with thy knife

c) • dissembly
• malefactors
• exhibition
• examine(d)

d) • rotten orange
• She's but the sign and semblance of her honour
• cunning sin
• She knows the heat of a luxurious bed
• Her blush is guiltiness

Page 68 Writing Your Answers

Q1 a) i) Yes

ii) • Who wrote hit after hit after hit

iii) If the works were hits then lots of people must have gone to see the plays.

b) i) • Lords, ladies and gents all rated his skills
• hit after hit after hit

ii) Repetition

iii) Repetition makes him sound even more popular — "lords, ladies and gents" sounds like all the important people liked Kit and "hit after hit" suggests an unlimited number of hits.

c) The writer says the geese didn't like Kit because he used the geese's feathers as quills to write his plays — "Each day he used up forty goose-feather quills".

Q2 Possible answer:
• The writer says that the play was like "a grand opera and a fireworks display rolled into one". This makes the play sound lavish like an opera and spectacular like a fireworks display.
• The fact that the writer says "Luke Matchett *lived* the title role" makes it sound as if he was doing more than acting and so was very convincing in the role.
• The writer says that Queen Margaret was "suitably evil", but the actress managed to convey an "underlying sadness". The fact that she's describing the actress doing two things at once shows that she's impressed.
• At the end of the review, the writer calls the play "An absolute triumph!". This is quite an over-the-top way of saying the performance was good so it shows she is really enthusiastic about it.

Page 69 Writing Your Answers

Q1 a) • Benedick and Beatrice have a very competitive relationship. They both try to prove they are more intelligent by constantly putting each other down. For example, Benedick calls Beatrice "a rare parrot-teacher", then she retorts by saying "a bird of my tongue is better than a beast of yours", trying to go one better than Benedick.

b)

Point	Quote
Beatrice suggests people find Benedick boring.	"Nobody marks you."
Beatrice says she never wants to get married.	"I had rather hear my dog bark at a crow than a man swear he loves me."
Benedick says Beatrice would be violent towards a husband.	"some gentleman or other shall scape a predestinate scratched face."
Benedick says Beatrice just repeats old sayings she's learnt.	"you are a rare parrot-teacher."

c) • The atmosphere in this extract is quite unpleasant but also comical. Benedick and Beatrice take it in turns to hurl insults at each other, creating a tense atmosphere. However, their remarks often sound rather like childish squabbling, e.g. "Scratching could not make it worse, an 'twere such a face as yours", which the audience would find funny.

Shakespeare — Character Questions

Page 70 What Characters Do

Q1 a) Richard — good with words, cunning, ruthless
Claudio — awkward, gullible, has a good reputation
Prospero — powerful, has a temper, caring

b) Richard
good with words — He wins Anne over despite his past.
cunning — He sets King Edward and Clarence against each other for his own benefit.
ruthless — He has his own relatives killed in his quest for power.
Claudio
awkward — He has to get Don Pedro to chat Hero up for him.
gullible — He's very quick to fall for Don John's tricks, and never suspects him of lying.
has a good reputation — The messenger says he acted bravely in the war.
Prospero
powerful — He uses his magic to create the storm.
has a temper — He treats Ariel and Caliban very harshly at times.
caring — He's happy for Miranda and Ferdinand.

Q2 a) "Spread a rumour that Anne is seriously ill."
"I'll make sure Anne doesn't go anywhere."
"Find a commoner to marry Clarence's daughter."
"Stop messing about!"

b) The extract shows that Richard is intelligent and organised, as he knows exactly what he needs to do to strengthen his position. It also shows that he is cold-hearted and ruthless, apparently planning the death of his wife without feeling at all guilty. The tone he uses also shows he is impatient and determined to succeed.

Page 71 What Characters Say

Q1 a) A — Benedick says he'll never get married.
B — Benedick says that you shouldn't be held to things you've said in the past.

b) A — because he wants to be seen as independent.

c) B — because he's changed his mind about getting married.

Q2 a) A — Prospero talks about how he and Miranda were banished from Milan.
B — Prospero says he forgives Antonio and Sebastian for betraying him and plotting against Alonso.

b) • forgiving
• determined
• moral

Q3 a) A — Come on everyone, get on with what you have to do. Let's not be scared by stupid dreams.
B — Let's be inspired by the passion and bravery of Saint George. Let's get them — we're bound to win.

b) • proud
• eloquent
• determined

Page 72 What Characters Say

Q1 a) i) Alonso is pessimistic. — He feels sure Ferdinand is dead.
ii) Alonso feels guilty. — He blames himself for what's happened to Ferdinand.
iii) Alonso is irritable. — He's annoyed when people try to cheer him up.

b) i) • "My son is lost"
• "What strange fish / Hath made his meal on thee?"
ii) "Would I had never / Married my daughter there, for coming thence / My son is lost."
iii) "You cram these words into mine ears against / The stomach of my sense."

Q2 a) i) Richard doesn't feel bad about killing the Princes. — Richard openly states his plans.
ii) Buckingham is unsure about Richard's request. — Buckingham asks for some time to think.
iii) Richard is impatient with Buckingham. — Richard repeats his question to Buckingham.

b) i) "I wish the bastards dead"
ii) "Give me some little breath, some pause, dear lord / Before I positively speak in this"
iii) "Say, have I thy consent that they shall die?"

Page 73 What Characters Say

Q1 Here's one way you could complete the table:

Comment	Explanation	Quote
Beatrice cares about what people think of her.	She decides to change the way she acts after people criticise her.	"Contempt, farewell, and maiden pride, adieu!"
She feels bad for the way she's treated Benedick.	She says she will return his love.	"I will requite thee, Taming my wild heart to thy loving hand."
She's not as clever as she thinks she is.	She's fallen for the trick.	"others say thou dost deserve, and I believe it better than reportingly."

Shakespeare Answers

Comment	Explanation	Quote
Prospero treats Caliban harshly.	He threatens him with painful punishments.	"thou shalt have cramps, Side-stiches that shall pen thy breath up"
In the past, Prospero was kind to Caliban.	He fed him well and taught him to speak.	"wouldst give me / Water with berries in't, and teach me how / To name the bigger light and how the less"
Caliban is bitter at Prospero.	He says Prospero stole the island from him.	"This island's mine by Sycorax my mother, Which thou tak'st from me."

Q3 *The answer to this one depends on which character you choose.*

Page 74 How Characters Think

Q1 a) He tells him to fetch some fuel.

b) Because he doesn't do it straightaway.

c) Because he is scared of the power of Prospero's magic.

Q2 A — ii)
B — iii)
C — i)

Q3 a) Because he thinks the other characters sounded too serious and genuine for it to be a trick.

b) Very effective — Benedick says "I hear how I am censured", and this seems to make him decide that he ought to return Beatrice's love.

Shakespeare — Language Questions

Page 75 Writing About Descriptions

Q1 a) Claudio saw Hero for the first time.
He liked Hero but didn't fall in love with her.
Claudio went to fight in the war.
After the war ended he had more time to think about love.
Claudio fell in love with Hero.

b) Any two valid answers, e.g.
- soldier's eye
- a rougher task in hand
- war-thoughts

c) Any valid answer, e.g.
- thronging soft and delicate desires
- how fair young Hero is

d) He describes his thoughts as if they are living in rooms in his head. He describes the "war-thoughts" leaving the rooms, and the "soft" thoughts of love moving in.

e) *The answers a)-d) should be used, in any order, to answer the question.*

Q2 *These are just some of the points you could make in your answer. Don't forget the quotes:*
- Anne says that Richard has "made the happy earth thy hell". This hints at the evil deeds that have gone on, and brings up the theme of death and killing.
- The phrase "pattern of thy butcheries" creates an impression of frequent violent acts.
- When Anne says that King Henry's wounds "Open their congealed mouths and bleed afresh", she creates a gruesome image of continuing pain and bloodshed.
- The description of Richard's deeds being "inhuman and unnatural" suggest he has acted like a savage monster.

Page 76 Writing About Imagery

Q1 A:

a) The way Beatrice speaks

b) Daggers

c) It tells us that Beatrice talks in a sharp, nasty way.

d) Benedick feels hurt by the way Beatrice has spoken to him.

e) One of the themes of the play is people using tricks and disguises. This quote shows how these tricks can be hurtful. Beatrice has pretended not to recognise Benedick and has said cruel things about him to his face. In the quote, Benedick compares this to being "stabbed."
B:

a) Richard

b) A spider

c) It suggests Richard is devious and dangerous, setting traps to lure people to their downfall.

d) Queen Margaret bitterly hates Richard and seems to be disgusted by him.

e) The comparison adds to the audience's impression of Richard being a hideous, evil killer, and hints at the killings and bloodshed that occur later on in the play. It also creates a lot of tension, as Queen Margaret clearly hates Richard.
C:

a) Caliban, Stephano and Trinculo, and how they will be tormented.

b) Leopards

c) They will be covered in spots from the painful magic spells, and in pain from cramps.

d) Prospero is determined to punish them for plotting against him.

e) It adds to our impression of the power of Prospero's magic, and also shows how merciless he can be when he is angry.

Q2 *4 points similar to these should get 8 marks.*
- The phrase "alabaster innocent arms" shows that the Princes were only young children who have done nothing to deserve their fate.
- Describing their lips as "four red roses" suggests they were young and healthy, making it seem even more tragic that they were murdered.
- The words "summer beauty" further adds to the sense of the cruelty of the Princes being murdered, because it contrasts with the violent act, and emphasises how the Princes are young and innocent, and have been murdered with their whole lives before them. This adds to the pity the audience feels for them.
- "A book of prayers" suggests they were good, religious children. This would further add to the sense of Richard's barbarism and cruelty in having the Princes murdered for his own benefit.

Shakespeare Answers

Page 77 Writing About the Mood

Q1 These are just a few things you could say.

	Setting	How the characters speak	Description & imagery	MOOD
A	The island	They speak in prose. Trinculo and Caliban insult each other a lot.	Trinculo calls Caliban a "monster" and a "natural".	Comical, aggressive
B	Leonato's house	Don John talks in prose, and uses long, complicated sentences.	Don John says he would rather be a "canker" than a "rose".	Depressed, sullen, bad-tempered
C	London	Elizabeth and Richard argue with each other. Margaret makes bitter aside comments.	Margaret says Elizabeth stole her position and calls Richard "devil".	Tense, hostile

Q2 *Use all the points you made in Q1 and don't forget to quote to back up everything you say.*

Page 78 Writing About Persuasive Language

Q1 <u>Says it will be very simple to kill Alonso:</u>
• If he were that which now he's like — that's dead —
Whom I with this obedient steel, three inches of it,
Can lay to bed for ever
<u>Scoffs at the idea of feeling guilty:</u>
•   Twenty consciences
That stand 'twixt me and Milan, candied be they,
And melt ere they molest!
<u>Says Gonzalo won't be a problem:</u>
• This ancient morsel, this Sir Prudence, who
Should not upbraid our course.
<u>Says no one else will stand in their way:</u>
•   For all the rest,
They'll take suggestion as a cat laps milk,
They'll tell the clock to any business that
We say befits the hour.

Q2 <u>Uses rhetorical questions:</u>
• Shall these enjoy our lands? Lie with our wives?
Ravish our daughters?
<u>Talks about past successes:</u>
•   these bastard Bretons, whom our fathers
Have in their own land beaten, bobbed, and thumped,
And in record left them the heirs of shame.
<u>Uses violent language to get soldiers ready for battle:</u>
• Let's whip these stragglers o'er the seas again,
Lash hence these overweening rags of France
• beaten, bobbed, and thumped
<u>Insults their enemies:</u>
• overweening rags of France
• famished beggars
• poor rats
• bastard Bretons
<u>Plays on fears of defeat:</u>
• If we be conquered, let men conquer us!
• Shall these enjoy our lands? Lie with our wives?
Ravish our daughters?
<u>Uses patriotic language to motivate soldiers:</u>
• our lands

Q3 *Whichever one you do, try to make as many points (backed up by quotes) as you can. You need to make at least six points (with quotes) to get full marks.*

Page 79 Revision Questions — Richard III

Q1 a) *e.g.*
• hateful withered hag
• stay, dog
• The worm of conscience still begnaw thy soul
• a hell of ugly devils
• Thou elvish-marked, abortive, rooting hog
• Thou rag of honour

b) i) • Queen Margaret feels bitterly angry at Richard. She clearly hates him and wishes bad luck and a miserable future on him.
• Richard is equally spiteful towards Margaret.
ii) • Richard describes Margaret as a "hateful, withered hag", making her seem old, ugly and scheming.
• Margaret describes Richard's deformed appearance and his premature birth — "sealed in thy nativity / The slave of Nature, and the son of hell" — making it seem that he was destined to be hideous and evil right from the start of his life.
iii) • The phrase "a hell of ugly devils" creates a frightening and bleak image. The fact that Margaret wishes them to visit Richard in his dreams shows how much she despises him.
• The imagery of Richard being an "elvish-marked, abortive, rooting hog" makes him appear inhuman and unnatural.
iv) • Margaret speaks in long sentences, allowing her to throw insult upon insult at Richard. Her sentences seem to gather momentum, culminating in phrases such as "Thou loathed issue of thy father's loins".
• Richard eventually stops Margaret in her tracks by interrupting her half-way through insulting him.
v) • The rhythm of Margaret's long speech starts off slow and steady, with complex phrases containing words with long vowel sounds such as "the worm of conscience still begnaw thy soul".
• The rhythm becomes quicker and sharper towards the end of the speech and when Richard tries to throw Margaret with one-word interruptions.

c) *If any of your quotes from a) aren't used in b) add a point for each one, e.g.:*
• When Margaret says "stay, dog", she tries to put Richard in his place by ordering him around like a badly behaved animal.
• The phrase "Thou rag of honour" seems to sum up Margaret's feelings that Richard has no sense of decency in him.

d) *Put the points in a sensible order. If there are any that don't really answer the question leave them out. If you think other points need to be made to answer the question add them in.*

e) *Use your plan from part d). You need to make at least six points with quotes to get full marks.*

Page 80 Revision Questions — The Tempest & Much Ado

Q1 a) *e.g.*
• elves
• demi-puppets

Shakespeare Answers

- moonshine
-                         I have bedimmed
The noontide sun
-                     the strong-based promontory
Have I made shake
-                             Graves at my command
Have waked their sleepers
- heavenly music

b) i) • Prospero is remembering all the powerful magical spells he has cast in the past. Now he feels ready to give up his magic for good.

ii) • The description of "ye that on the sands with printless foot / Do chase the ebbing Neptune" gives the speech a mythical feel, as it sounds like a fairy tale or a legend rather than real life.

• The phrases "dread rattling thunder" and "Jove's stout oak" create a sense of the formidable power of nature, adding to the impression of how powerful Prospero's magic must be to be able to control them.

iii) • The imagery of "azured vault" to describe the sky gives an impression of its vastness and its deep blue colour.

iv) • Prospero's sentences are mostly long and complex. This allows him to list all the magical beings he has power over. The long sentences sound impressive and mystical, adding to the mysterious, magical mood.

v) • The rhythm is slow and steady, allowing Prospero to sound commanding and powerful, gradually building up an impression of the range and power of his magic.

c) *If any of your quotes from a) aren't used in b) add a point for each one, e.g.:*

• Mythical creatures such as "elves" and "demi-puppets" set the scene for the magical, unbelievable events that Prospero describes.

• Prospero's powers sometimes seem to extend even to waking the dead, as in "Graves at my command / Have waked their sleepers".

• The "moonshine" suggests that the events happen at night, with the glow of the moon creating a spooky, magical atmosphere.

d) *Put the points in a sensible order. If there are any that don't really answer the question leave them out. If you think other points need to be made to answer the question add them in.*

e) *Use your plan from part d). You need to make at least six points with quotes to get full marks.*

Q2 a) *e.g.*
- not the unhopefullest husband
- humour your cousin
- queasy stomach
- we are the only love-gods

b) i) • Don Pedro is feeling in a good mood — he talks in a friendly, humorous way, e.g. "If we can do this, Cupid is no longer an archer".

• Don Pedro is thinking about a way to get Benedick and Beatrice together, e.g. he says he will teach Hero how to "humour your cousin, that she shall fall in love with Benedick."

ii) • Don Pedro describes Benedick as "not the unhopefullest husband that I know" which is quite a humorous description — a back-handed compliment.

• Don Pedro describes Benedick's good qualities, e.g.

"approved valour and confirmed honesty", which shows he values him as a friend. This means the idea of the trick seems light-hearted, rather than nasty — because we know that Don Pedro would want the best for his friend.

• Don Pedro's description of Benedick's "queasy stomach" is quite funny. It suggests that Benedick is a bit touchy and easily scared off from things.

iii) • Don Pedro uses a humorous image, saying he and his friends will be the "the only love-gods", if they can manage to get Benedick and Beatrice together. He says that Cupid will be out of a job and they will replace him.

iv) • The sentences are quite long. Don Pedro is talking to his friends in a relaxed way.

v) • The rhythm is quite lively and choppy, e.g. "If we can do this, Cupid is no longer an archer: his glory shall be ours, for we are the only love-gods." Don Pedro sounds excited and energetic.

c) *If any of your quotes from a) aren't used in b) add a point for each one.*

d) *Put the points in a sensible order. If there are any that don't really answer the question leave them out. If you think other points need to be made to answer the question add them in.*

e) *Use your plan from part d). You need to make at least six points with quotes to get full marks.*

Shakespeare — Performance Questions
Page 81 Performance — The Basics

Q1 a) • They are both in either's pow'rs, but this swift business
I must uneasy make, lest too light winning
Make the prize light.

b) thoughtful, quiet

c) forceful, loud, angry, accusatory

Q2 • At the start of the extract, Benedick is his usual confident self. He boldly tells Don Pedro and Claudio that he'll never marry, responding to Don Pedro's "savage bull" remark with clever word-play: "pluck off the bull's horns".

• As Don Pedro and Claudio continue to make fun out of him, Benedick becomes less confident and more defensive. He tries to keep control of the conversation with the "earthquake" comment, but by the end of the extract he is annoyed at the mockery from the other characters.

• In the end, he loses his sense of humour and seems to become quite sensitive. He says "examine your conscience", telling off Don Pedro and Claudio before walking off in a temper.

Page 82 How Characters Speak

Q1 a,b) *And stops he now for breath?*
• annoyed — he's annoyed that Buckingham has suddenly stopped supporting him wholeheartedly.
• impatient, angry
I will take order for her keeping close
• assertive — he's taking charge of the plan to strengthen his position as king
• confident, determined
Look how thou dream'st! I say again, give out

That Anne, my queen, is sick and like to die.
• impatient — he's telling off Catesby for hanging around and wants him to get on with it.
• assertive, annoyed, commanding, angry
Uncertain way of gain!
• regretful — he realises it's not a perfect plan.
• annoyed, worried
Tear-falling pity dwells not in this eye
• remorseless — he feels no pity for his victims
• single-minded, determined

Q2 *You could say something like this:*

• *O good Gonzalo ... word and deed!*
He could emphasise his gratitude and good will towards Gonzalo by speaking clearly and slowly.
• *Most cruelly ... furtherer in the act*
He should sound angry and reproachful, to emphasise his bitterness about what Alonso and Sebastian did. He should sound calm though, as he has had plenty of time to think about what happened.
• *Thou art pinched for't now, Sebastian!*
Prospero could raise his voice at this point, perhaps emphasising the word "pinched", to show his satisfaction that Sebastian is being punished for what he did.
• *Flesh and blood ... unnatural though thou art.*
Prospero would again sound angry, but could also have a disbelieving, incredulous tone, to show he is still shocked and hurt that his own brother could betray him.
• *Their understanding ... or would know me.*
Prospero would have a fairly neutral tone for these lines, as he is simply commenting on the fact that his enemies are coming back to their senses after the spell.
• *Ariel, / Fetch me the hat and rapier in my cell.*
He should sound slightly more urgent and businesslike at this point, as he is about to put into place the final part of his plan — he wants to be in the clothes he wore when he was Duke of Milan, so that his appearance in front of his enemies has maximum effect.

Page 83 How Characters Move

Q1 a) • *Look to the drawbridge there!*
Richard should point to the drawbridge of the Tower.
• *Catesby, o'erlook the walls!*
Richard should face Catesby and direct him to the Tower walls.
• *Look back, defend thee!*
Richard should point behind Buckingham, to the back of the stage.
• *Enter* LOVELL *and* RATCLIFFE, *with Hastings' head.*
Lovell and Ratcliffe walk onto the stage. This could be quite gruesome — they could hold the head so that it's really obvious to the audience, for more impact.

b) • Buckingham could stop still and cup his hand to his ear as he says, "Hark! A drum".
• Lovell could hold out Hastings' head to Richard when he says, "Here is the head of that ignoble traitor". Again, this could be made quite gruesome.

Q2 • Claudio could turn to walk away from Leonato when he says "I will not have to do with you."
• During the next two lines, Leonato could move to stand

in Claudio's way to stop him from leaving. Leonato could point to himself when he says "thou shalt kill a man."
• When Antonio starts talking, he could come over to stand next Leonato, to show he's on his side, directly facing Claudio in a confrontational way.
• When Leonato says "Brother", he could turn to put his hand on Antonio's chest, to try to calm him down and discourage him from getting into a fight with Claudio.

Q3 • When Prospero says the words "foul conspiracy" he could have a disgusted expression on his face, to show his contempt for Caliban and his fellow plotters.
• When Prospero says "Well done! Avoid", he could turn towards the spirits who have been acting in the masque, and possibly gesture impatiently for them to go away, to show he needs to deal with Caliban as quickly as possible.
• Ferdinand should frown in confusion when he says "This is strange", to emphasise his surprise at Prospero's sudden change in mood.
• Miranda could have a worried expression on her face at seeing him "so distempered", to show she is concerned because Prospero doesn't usually act like this.

Page 84 Revision Questions — Richard III

Q1 a) • 1st chunk — Buckingham and Richard pretend to be friendly to Prince Edward as he arrives at the Tower. The Prince is annoyed at the complications of the journey and that Richard won't allow his relatives to be with him.
• 2nd chunk — Richard tells Prince Edward that he is too young to realise that his uncles are actually a lot nastier than they seem. The Prince disagrees.
• 3rd chunk — The Mayor of London arrives and greets Prince Edward. The Prince wonders why his mother, Queen Elizabeth, and his brother, the Duke of York, haven't arrived yet. Then Hastings finally turns up to bring news about where they have been.

b) Buckingham:
i) • 1st chunk — to Prince Edward
• 3rd chunk — could be to any or all of the characters
ii) • 1st chunk — he is trying to appear pleasant to Prince Edward — "sweet Prince"
• 3rd chunk — he seems amused by Hastings' late arrival — "in good time, here comes the sweating lord".
iii) • 1st chunk — he could bend down towards the Prince in a patronising way, to show he is going over the top to appear nice to him.
• 3rd chunk — he could cast his hand in the direction of Hastings, to draw more attention to him.
iv) • 1st chunk — overly pleasant, to show how hard he is trying.
• 3rd chunk — amused by Hastings' arrival.
v) • 1st chunk — "sweet prince"
• 3rd chunk — "sweating"

Richard:
i) • all chunks — to Prince Edward
ii) • 1st and 3rd chunks — like Buckingham, he is trying to appear pleasant to the Prince — "dear cousin".
• 2nd chunk — he tries to seem like he has the Prince's best interests at heart. He tries to sound like he is passing

Shakespeare Answers

on valuable advice and looking after him —"God keep you from them, and from such false friends!".

iii) • 1st chunk — he could speak face-to-face to the Prince, to show he is trying to appear genuine and friendly.
• 2nd chunk — he could wag his finger at the Prince when he says "God keep you from them", to emphasise that he wants to seem like he is giving him good advice.
• 3rd chunk — he could gesture towards the Mayor with a reassuring smile, to try to stop the Prince being suspicious about his uncles not being there.

iv) • all chunks — he should sound overly pleasant and friendly, to show that he is over-compensating for his evil plans by being extra nice to the Prince.

v) • 1st chunk — "dear cousin"
• 2nd chunk — "dangerous", "poison", "false friends"
• 3rd chunk — none

Prince Edward:

i) • 1st and 2nd chunks — Richard
• 3rd chunk — all the other characters

ii) • 1st chunk — tired and worried that his uncles aren't there — "tedious, wearisome and heavy".
• 2nd chunk — sceptical about Richard's claims that his uncles are dangerous — "but they were none".
• 3rd chunk — confused about the absence of Queen Elizabeth and the Duke of York, and annoyed at Hastings' lateness — "what a slug is Hastings".

iii) • 1st chunk — he could shake his head as he says "No, uncle".
• 2nd chunk — again he could shake his head, to emphasise his disagreement with Richard.
• 3rd chunk — he could look around him anxiously as he asks for signs of Queen Elizabeth and the Duke of York.

iv) • 1st chunk — tired and frustrated at his difficult journey.
• 2nd chunk — assertive as he says "but they were none".
• 3rd chunk — polite but anxious at first, but annoyed when he talks about Hastings.

v) • 1st chunk — "tedious, wearisome and heavy"
• 2nd chunk — "none"
• 3rd chunk — "slug"

Lord Mayor:
i) • 3rd chunk — to Prince Edward.
ii) • 3rd chunk — he seems unaware of the tension between the other characters — "God bless your Grace".
iii) • 3rd chunk — he should enter the scene calmly and confidently.
iv) • 3rd chunk — he should sound polite and respectful towards the Prince.
v) • 3rd chunk — none

c) *Try to use as many points from b) as you can in your answer. You need to make at least six points with quotes to get full marks.*

Page 85 Revision Questions — Much Ado & The Tempest

Q1 *This is the kind of thing you could include in your answer:*
i) In this extract, Leonato is talking to the Friar and Beatrice.

ii) • Leonato is feeling very angry and upset, because he believes the accusations that Hero has been having an affair. For example, he says that he hopes Hero is dead: "Do not live, Hero, do not ope thine eyes."
• He also feels ashamed and betrayed that his beloved daughter could have behaved in such a fashion: "mine I loved...she is fallen / Into a pit of ink."

iii) • When he says "Why ever wast thou lovely in my eyes?", the actor playing Leonato could shake his head in amazement, to show how strange it seems to him that he could ever have thought Hero was lovely.
• For the line "Dost thou look up?", Leonato could turn to look down at Hero.

iv) • During the three lines that start with "Wherefore!" the actor playing Leonato could speak in an outraged tone, to show that he thinks the answer to the Friar's question is obvious.
• When Leonato says "O Fate!", his voice could be shaking emotionally.
• When he says "Grieved I", and for the next few lines, Leonato could seem even more sad and reflective, rather than angry. He could use a quiet, regretful tone.

v) • The actor playing Leonato could end the speech with a flourish when he says the words "foul-tainted flesh!", throwing his head back to show how disgusted he is with Hero.
• For the lines that begin "But mine", Leonato's voice could get louder with each time the word "mine" is repeated, to show how he's getting more and more emotional the more he thinks about his daughter.

Q2 *This is the kind of thing you could think about for your answer:*
Trinculo
i) To himself
ii) He's bemused by Caliban — he's only just worked out that he's a person and not a fish. He's concerned about taking shelter from the storm — "there is no other shelter hereabout".
iii) He could leap back from Caliban when he says "Warm, o' my troth!", to show he is startled to find out Caliban is alive. When he creeps under Caliban's cloak, he could do so tentatively, to show he is wary of him.
iv) He should sound nervous and unsure of what the best thing to do is. When he says "this is no fish, but an islander", he could sound shocked at the discovery.
v) "o' my troth!"

Stephano
i) He is singing and talking to himself.
ii) He is drunk and seems amused by the discovery of Caliban — "Have we devils here?".
iii) He could stagger about from side to side to show how drunk he is. When he drinks he should swig the wine straight from the bottle, possibly spilling some down his chin.
iv) He should slur his words quite a lot. When he finds Caliban he should sound quite excited and intrigued, as he can't work out what he is at first. When he says "I have not scaped drowning to be afeard now of your four legs", he should sound assured and defiant, to show he is not afraid.
v) "devils", "Ha!"

Shakespeare Answers

Caliban
i) In his first line he is pleading with Stephano. In his second line he is talking to himself.
ii) He feels frightened and doesn't know what is happening — "Do not torment me."
iii) He could cower under his cloak, hiding his head, to show he is afraid and trying to avoid being seen.
iv) He could speak in a high-pitched shriek, or his voice could be shaking with fear.
v) "O!"

Shakespeare — Ideas, Themes and Issues

Page 86 Ideas, Themes and Issues in Richard III

Q1 a,b) • *curtailed of this fair propotion,*
Richard says he's been denied a normal human appearance.
• *Cheated of feature by dissembling Nature*
He feels nature hasn't given him the impressive looks he deserves.
•   *scarce half made up,*
And that so lamely and unfashionable
That dogs bark at me as I halt by them
Richard says that because he was prematurely born, he wasn't properly formed, and as a result he is so ugly that even dogs bark at him.
• *Unless to spy my shadow in the sun*
And descant on mine own deformity.
He is reminded of his ugliness wherever he goes, so he is given plenty of opportunity to think about it.

c) • Richard seems to be bitter about his ugly appearance.
• He seems to think that the way people act is affected by what they look like. So, instead of trying in vain to be loved and admired, he might as well live up to his ugly appearance by being a villain.

d) • Shakespeare may be suggesting that the way someone looks can affect their character.
• He may also be commenting that the way people can treat each other based on appearances can have negative consequences.

Q2 *These are some of the things you could write about.*

a, b) • *Let me sit heavy on thy soul tomorrow.*
Think how thou stab'st me in my prime of youth
At Tewkesbury; despair therefore, and die.
• *Let me sit heavy in thy soul tomorrow —*
I, that was washed to death with fulsome wine,
Poor Clarence, by thy guile betrayed to death —
Tomorrow in the battle think of me,
And fall thy edgeless sword; despair and die.
• *When I was mortal, my anointed body*
By thee was punched full of deadly holes.
Think of the Tower and me: despair and die!
The ghosts remind Richard and the audience of all his evil crimes in the past. They want his bad deeds to come back to haunt him, and suggest that he cannot win because he is evil.
• *Be cheerful, Richmond, for the wronged souls*
Of butchered princes fight in thy behalf
• *Virtuous and holy, be thou conqueror:*
Harry, that prophesied thou shouldst be King,
Doth comfort thee in thy sleep. Live and flourish!
• *Thou offspring of the House of Lancaster,*
The wronged heirs of York do pray for thee.

Good angels guard thy battle; live and flourish.
The ghosts of the people Richard has murdered are supporting Richmond to win the battle, because he is good. They want him to succeed and to live a long, healthy life.

c) • The ghosts support Richmond because he is good, and want him to win. They want Richard to remember his evil deeds, and for him to lose the battle as punishment.

d) • Shakespeare seems to suggest that justice will always be done eventually.
• Evil people should expect to punished for their crimes, and good people will be rewarded for their good deeds.
You need to make at least 6 points properly backed up with quotes to get 18 marks.

Page 87 Ideas, Themes and Issues in The Tempest

Q1 a,b) • *the sea, which hath requit it*
The sea has avenged the betrayal of Prospero by bringing his enemies to the island.
• *The pow'rs, delaying, not forgetting, have*
Incensed the seas and shores, yea, all the creatures,
Against your peace.
Fate is not going to let Alonso and his followers escape punishment for their crimes.
•   *Thee of thy son, Alonso,*
They have bereft, and do pronounce by me
Ling'ring perdition, worse than any death
Can be at once, shall step by step attend
You and your ways
Ariel announces that fate is punishing Alonso by taking his son away from him and leading him into eternal ruin.
•   *heart's sorrow,*
And a clear life ensuing
Alonso will be left to reflect on his actions, in order to clear his conscience.

c) • Ariel is saying that all the problems and disasters that have befallen Alonso since the shipwreck are a direct punishment for how he treated Prospero in the past. He says that fate is ensuring that justice is done.

d) • Shakespeare seems to be saying that, no matter how long people think they have got away with doing something bad, justice will always be done in the end.

Q2 a,b) •   *Your charm so strongly works 'em*
That if you now beheld them your affections
Would become tender.
Ariel says that, if Prospero could see how much his enemies are suffering from his spells, he would feel really sorry for them.
• *Hast thou, which art but air, a touch, a feeling*
Of their afflictions, and shall not myself,
One of their kind, that relish all as sharply,
Passion as they, be kindlier moved than thou art?
Prospero says that, if Ariel, who is only a spirit of the air, can feel sorry for them, then he, as a human being, should feel even more sympathy.
• *Though with their high wrongs I am struck to th' quick,*
Yet with my nobler reason 'gainst my fury
Do I take part. The rarer action is
In virtue than in vengeance.
Even though Prospero is still angry about how he was betrayed, he's determined to be reasonable and not be ruled by his negative feelings. He says it is more honourable to forgive than to take revenge.

Shakespeare Answers

•   *They being penitent,*
The sole drift of my purpose doth extend
Not a frown further.
Prospero says that, if his enemies are sorry for what they've done, then his plan is complete and he doesn't need to punish them any more.
c) • Prospero values forgiveness more highly than revenge. He thinks that, if people are sorry for their bad deeds, they should be forgiven, not punished repeatedly.

d) • Shakespeare shows that it is possible to forgive your enemies, no matter how badly they have treated you in the past.
• He suggests that the noblest thing to do is to forgive, rather than take revenge.

Page 88 Ideas, Themes and Issues in Much Ado About Nothing

Q1 a,b) • *for which of my bad parts didst thou first fall in love with me?*
Benedick asks why Beatrice fell in love with him, joking about how they used to hate each other.
• *for which of my good parts did you first suffer love for me?*
Beatrice asks Benedick the same question.
• *Suffer love! A good epithet! I do suffer love indeed, for I love thee against my will.*
Benedick says he has no choice about being in love, and that it's painful for him.
• *I will never love that which my friend hates.*
Beatrice uses word-play to avoid saying outright that she loves Benedick.
• *Thou and I are too wise to woo peaceably.*
Benedick says they'll never be simply romantic towards each other — they'll always be debating things.

c) • Both Benedick and Beatrice were very cynical about love at the start of the play.
• Now they have admitted they are in love, but still don't claim to see it in a very romantic way.
• They say that they have no choice about loving each other.

d) • Shakespeare shows that love isn't as straightforward and romantic as some people think it is.
• Love can be closely linked to hate.
• Everyone is capable of love, even those who claim that they will never be in love.

Q2 a,b) • *There was never counterfeit of passion came so near the life of passion as she discovers it.*
Leonato says, as part of the trick, that there's no way Beatrice could have been pretending to be in love, as it was too convincing.
• *Bait the hook well — this fish will bite.*
Claudio says if they make the idea of Beatrice being in love appealing enough, Benedick will fall for the trick.
• *I should think this is a gull, but that the white-bearded fellow speaks it. Knavery cannot, sure, hide himself in such reverence.*
Benedick says he'd think it was a trick if it wasn't for the fact that Leonato is involved.
• *He hath ta'en the infection. Hold it up.*
Claudio tells the other tricksters, Don Pedro and Leonato, that Benedick has fallen for the trick, and encourages them to keep it going.

c) • Claudio sees the trick as a harmless game.
• Leonato and Don Pedro seem to find it fun too.
• Benedick believes that old, respectable-looking people couldn't possibly be involved in trickery.

d) • In this scene, Shakespeare shows that trickery can be well-meaning and harmless.
• The trick is visually comical, with Benedick hiding in a bush.
• It's also funny because Benedick thinks of himself as being clever, but he completely falls for the trick.